SUCCESS
PLANNING
MANUAL

I have yet to read the life story of a truly great successful man, whether he be artist, businessman, doctor, lawyer, statesman, inventor, scientist, or what have you, who did not achieve success by great desire and careful planning.

THEY ORGANIZE THEIR MOST VALUABLE RESOURCE—"THEMSELVES"

They PLAN—then ACT—then GROW.

NOW, YOU can plan, record, and organize YOUR complete personal and business affairs, past—present—future, in this one single volume.

Make the most of yourself, for that is all there is to you.
                    —Ralph Waldo Emerson

SUCCESS
PLANNING
MANUAL

EXECUTIVE METHODS
TO INCREASE YOUR WORTH

by

ALFRED ARMAND MONTAPERT

YOUR PERSONAL
- *PLANS*
- *GOALS*
- *RECORDS*
- *DEVELOPMENT*
- *ACHIEVEMENTS*

To each is given a set of tools,
An hour-glass and a book of rules,
And each must build ere his time is flown
A stumbling block or a stepping stone.

Your life will be no better than the plans you make and the action you take. You are the architect and builder of your own life, fortune, destiny.

LIBRARY OF CONGRESS
CATALOG CARD NUMBER: 67–12652

PRINTED IN THE UNITED STATES OF AMERICA
85920 — B & P

SUCCESS PLANNING MANUAL

You have the Power
to get "What You Want" out of life . . .
If . . . You know what you want!!
If . . . You have a Plan to guide you!

* CONFIDENTIAL *

This comprehensive manual is designed primarily for personal achievement and to help keep your personal affairs in order. It applies executive methods to increase your worth in all areas of your life: planning, financial, personal, occupation and business, health, mental, family and home, travel and culture, social, spiritual, and retirement. The essence of this Planning Manual covers the scope of your complete life, and contains profitable planning suggestions for your personal success and fortune.

Keep in a safe place. Study, revise, and upgrade it — often.

By The Same Author

DISTILLED WISDOM
"Thoughts That Successful Men Live By"

ACKNOWLEDGMENTS

Sincere thanks are extended to the publishers and individuals for permission to include material in this work. Our grateful acknowledgment to:

Dartnell Corp. for use of "Executive Self-Rating Chart" from *What An Executive Should Know About Himself,* by J. C. Penney.

Feather, William, for use of the article "This Is Business," by William Feather.

Forbes Publishing Co. for use of the article "YOU" from *The Keys to Success* by B. C. Forbes.

Hill, Napoleon, for use of selected material in Personal Analysis from *Think and Grow Rich,* by Dr. Napoleon Hill.

Hormel News Magazine for use of the article "Every Family Should Have."

Mayo, Charles W., for use of the article "Health Tips" by Charles W. Mayo.

Stowers, Harvey, for use of the article "Faces and What They Say."

The short quotations used in this book were taken from DISTILLED WISDOM by Alfred Armand Montapert, Prentice-Hall, Inc.

DEDICATED

To you the reader, who becomes the associate writer of this Manual. May you realize that happiness and success in life do not depend on your circumstances, but on yourself. May the whole story of your life be uplifted and benefited a thousand fold.

THIS IS THE PERSONAL MANUAL OF

NAME

ADDRESS

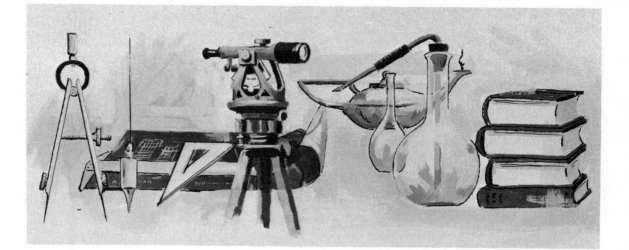

TOMORROW'S SUCCESS IS THE RESULT OF TODAY'S PLANNING!
Most failures and miseries can be traced directly back to a lack of wise thinking beforehand.

WHAT THIS BOOK IS

A WORKING MANUAL CONTAINING. . . .

 . . . Suggestions to keep my personal affairs in order
 . . . Executive methods to increase my worth in all areas of my life
 . . . The location of all my important papers
 . . . My plans and procedures for personal achievement
 . . . My personal aims, motives, and desires
 . . . My personal records
 . . . The list of goals I wish to attain
 . . . My positive code for worthwhile living
 . . . My program for self-development
 . . . The record of my accomplishments
 . . . My patterns, formulas, techniques, for a successful career.

The records and suggestions contained in this comprehensive Manual give me principles and ideas on how to obtain and maintain good health, financial security, more free time from the tasks of making a living, techniques and ideas on learning, living, and achieving, my personal objectives.

A RECORD OF MY. . . .

 . . . Education
 . . . Employment
 . . . Finances and financial plans
 . . . Insurance
 . . . Health
 . . . Earthly possessions
 . . . Places I have travelled
 . . . Places I plan to travel
 . . . Family history
 . . . Friends and advisors
 . . . Retirement plans and my estate

This is my complete plan to organize and simplify my whole life . . . My guide for a well-balanced view of life . . . My outline of what I have yet to do . . . My material desires, as well as my personal self-development and enjoyments . . . My chart for the road ahead.

WHO AM I? Have I identified myself as an individual to the point I have become acquainted with myself?

WHAT DO I STAND FOR? Have I defined my basic beliefs?

WHERE AM I GOING IN LIFE? What are my objectives? What are my goals?

HOW AM I GOING TO GET THERE? Do I have a plan? Do I intend to make something happen?

Each man's life is a *PERSONAL* matter, and the steps to achievement are not the same for any two people. *YOUR SUCCESS* must necessarily be "authored" by *YOU*.

Every word written in this Manual and every picture is for the purpose of helping you to establish a set of personal records and develop a sound set of beneficial plans, to create a success blueprint for your personal journey from where you are now, to where you want to be.

ONE OF THE MOST IMPORTANT THINGS YOU WILL EVER DO IN LIFE IS THE PROPER PLANNING AND ORGANIZING OF YOUR LIFE!

This Personal Planning Manual can be invaluable in helping you to systematically develop and maintain a sound, beneficial, personal plan for your life. It can be used by every person who wants to build a positive code for worthwhile living. It contains techniques and ideas to develop your full potential and help you to enjoy the best life possible.

Socrates said: *Man, know thyself*. When filled in, this Manual gives a complete picture of yourself. It tells your whole personal story. It is interesting and unique and full of useful ideas. There is nothing like it on the market. It is especially designed to fill a neglected personal need. Almost all intelligent men lack an effective method of planning for success.

Today we live in a turbulent society. Days pass quickly, often complicated by pressures, demands and changes. We drive hard to satisfy certain desires and needs. The business of living is so demanding that we have neither the time nor methods to get fully organized. We rarely take time out to seriously meditate and establish our real purpose and goals in life.

Yet life belongs to those who organize and truly live it. Successful men invariably follow a pattern or formula that leads to success. They develop the habit of conducting their lives by plan and purpose.

The purpose of this Manual is to help you *PLAN, ORGANIZE, SIMPLIFY,* and *GUIDE* your life. Within its pages is set forth the complete chart of a lifetime. It is designed with appropriate headings and has ruled-in convenient spaces for the purpose of recording the important facts and personal plans which affect your life. By filling out the easy-to-understand forms you will be guided by your complete personal record, your accomplishments, your plans and goals.

Often circumstances arise in which reliable personal information becomes an immediate, vital necessity. No longer will the user of this Manual have to commit to memory bits and pieces of valuable knowledge or maintain numerous files and lists that all too often cannot be located when needed. You will save time and money and avoid the aspirin-and-black-coffee sessions—shuffling between hazy memory and a heap of disorganized papers. *ALL VITAL* information can now be assembled in this one complete Manual.

Why keep records? Why make plans? The run-of-the-mill individual, who is destined to go nowhere, regards records and plans as something to be avoided. The top-notcher sees them for what they are: an opportunity for self-diagnosis, improvement in efficiency, greater happiness, health and wealth. Records and plans help to review your failures and accomplishments. They give you the basis for analyzing and intelligently planning your life for the days and months ahead.

Every individual needs a re-cap of his background and career, in order to observe objectively if his desires are being accomplished. Whether in business or in our personal affairs, there comes a time when it seems appropriate to do some stock-taking. It is always proper to examine our past so that we may better chart our course for tomorrow. Your *Personal Planning Manual* fulfills this need.

This dynamic book was written especially for *YOU*. It is designed to help you make the most efficient and effective use of your life. Overall, it carries the "self-help" theme to a new stage. We do not know of any book that covers all areas of your life which engages the reader actively in the way this book does; providing the charts, questionnaires, etc., which cause you to take action step by step, shifting plans and hopes from the vague to the specific, and forcing you to take stock realistically by putting everything down on paper. The development of the book follows from a clear plan, and each section is logically organized (going from general concepts and discussions to specific action).

In the pages that follow you will find new ideas, techniques and some helpful suggestions designed to take a bit of guesswork out of your day-to-day living. This is a working Manual which you can use to help you along the road to personal achievement. It will help you to get your plans into sharper focus and to achieve improved results in your future growth.

The author has been out on the front lines of business for over forty years. Here he gives you the benefit of his wide experience and his own personal planning ideas and guides which have proven practical and effective. His success in life was achieved by following these plans, principles, and techniques. In addition, other material has been drawn from the words and thoughts of the famous and illustrious.

This is your own confidential Planning Manual. Refer to it constantly for your personal data and plans, and it will become one of your most cherished and useful possessions. It is designed to act as your silent travelling companion to help make your journey through life successful and happy.

Alfred Armand Montapert

What I need is somebody to make me do what I can.
—Emerson

YOU HAVE
THE POWER
TO GET WHAT
YOU WANT
OUT OF LIFE

CONTENTS

THE PROBLEM:

We live in the age of technological change and development. It is true that we have acquired a great deal of technical knowledge in recent years, but we have also made the business of living more confused and complicated. Thousands of men are *ALMOST* successful. Why should not man, having established his mastery over energy and matter, extend this same mastery over himself?

A man has failed to the degree that he has failed to use his God-given abilities to their fullest.

The average man wastes 30 to 60 percent of his time through lack of organization.

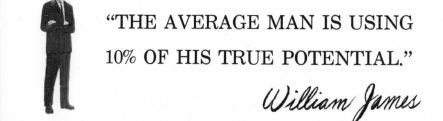

"THE AVERAGE MAN IS USING 10% OF HIS TRUE POTENTIAL."

William James

THE SOLUTION:

Organize your most valuable resource—*YOURSELF*—by *Planning* and *Action*.

PLANNED ACTION

If the architect must have his plans and the construction engineer must have his blueprints to build the building, how *MUCH MORE* do we need a set of *PLANS* to build our lives.

The builder of a good life *MUST* have his plans for the years ahead. The greatest responsibility given to each one of us is to develop ourselves.

One way to help accomplish this is to apply the principles in this Manual. Plan and improve each of the different departments of your life: *FINANCIAL—PERSONAL—BUSINESS—HEALTH—MENTAL—FAMILY AND HOME—TRAVEL AND CULTURE—SOCIAL—SPIRITUAL—RETIREMENT*.

PLANNING is a *MUST* in order to build a good life. Write down all the *PLANS—OBJECTIVES—GOALS* you want to accomplish in the next five years. Keep adding to these. Then break them down into steps. This is what makes it *easier*. This is what makes it *possible*.

A building is built, brick by brick. A painting is achieved stroke by stroke. A book is written word by word. Success is acquired step by step. *STEP BY STEP—STEP BY STEP*. There is no other way.

Life is like a grand staircase—some people are going up, and some people are going down. The direction of your life, whether you go up or down, will depend on the *PLANS* you make, and the *ACTION* you take.

YOU are the architect and builder of your own *LIFE—FORTUNE—DESTINY*.

This message can be wrapped up in two words—*MAKE PLANS!*

Set before yourself a great and definite life purpose. Hidden away in your innermost soul is a transcendent ideal capable of realization. What you need is not more capacity or greater opportunity, but increased resolution and concentration. Nothing will give you so much pleasure as the consciousness of making daily progress toward a great life purpose.

—Grenville Kleiser

To have a great purpose to work for, a purpose larger than ourselves, is one of the secrets of making life significant. Successful careers are motivated by great desires.

Instructions On How To Use This Planning Manual

THIS IS YOUR BOOK AND YOU ARE ITS ASSOCIATE WRITER. Fill out all the information you can in this book—it is the record of your life, and contains your plans for the future. You are the scribe. No year, month, day, hour or minute can be recalled or relived. Your life will be no better than the plans you make and the action you take. This book is designed to organize and simplify your life.

This book can be a practical help and guide. It promotes orderliness, spells out what you have to work with, gives an opportunity for consideration and corrections, clarifies your purposes; it helps formulate a workable plan, and will give a chart of your life instead of a haphazard way of trying to remember all the important events, data, and plans in your life.

When completed it will contain your biographical record, birth, education, employment, accomplishments, financial records, money management, plans, goals, aims, motives, desires, health, thoughts, hobbies, travel, culture, retirement, estate planning and miscellaneous helpful data.

Many unforeseen things happen to all of us. When they occur you can look over your planning record and make the most efficient changes in your plans, as you have a complete chart to go by.

In the management of your life, the question for each man to settle, is not what he would do if he had money, time, influence, and educational advantages; but what he will do with the things he has. Every man's heart cries out for a better life. You will enjoy reviewing your manual, improving your life and upgrading your records. It will keep you aware of your progress in all areas of your life.

Write upon the pages of this book the important data about *YOU* and *YOURS*. Then, with your notations and plans, these vital, priceless pages will spring into life.

We suggest that notations for permanent items such as social security numbers, vital statistics, educational records, etc., that will not change, be made in ink; and that pencil be used for all records subject to change.

You will have fun gathering and organizing all this data; it will be one of the most important things you can do. It is your chart for personal achievement. We wish you success in all your ventures.

IMPORTANT PAPERS AND WHERE TO FIND THEM

Disorder, seems to me something like as if a husband-man should throw into his granery barley, wheat, and peas together, and then, when he wants barley bread or wheaten bread, or pea soup should have to extract them grain by grain, instead of having them separate-ly laid up for his use.

—John Lubbock

1. PERSONAL RECORDS   LOCATION

a). Birth Certificate_____
b). Marriage Certificate_____
c). Last Will and Testament_____
d). Passport_____
e). Citizenship papers_____
f). Military service records_____
g). School diplomas_____
h). Credit Cards: Name_____Number_____
_____
i). Licenses_____

2. BUSINESS AND EMPLOYMENT RECORDS

a). Social Security Card Number_____
b). Employment Contracts_____
c). Important letters_____
d). Business licenses_____
e). Contracts relating to my business_____
f). Patents_____

3. FINANCIAL

a). Cash_____
b). Bank books_____
c). Stock and bond certificates_____
d). Other securities_____
e). Money you owe (Notes)_____
f). Money due you (Notes)_____
g). Bank accounts_____

4. PERSONAL PROPERTY

a). Safe deposit boxes_____
b). Personal safe_____
c). Jewelry_____
d). Coin collection_____
e). Stamp collection_____
f). Heirlooms_____
g). Household inventory_____
h). Automobile: Ownership records_____
    Drivers License_____Renewal Date_____

IMPORTANT PAPERS AND WHERE TO FIND THEM

Classification and system are now applied with great
advantage to all branches of education, business, and
other departments of human effort. Grouping ideas,
and objects into classes simplifies thinking. The
right use of system economizes thought, time and
energy.
                                    --Grenville Kleiser

5. TAX DATA   LOCATION
    a). Income tax returns_____
    b). Property tax receipts_____
    c). Business tax receipts_____

6. REAL PROPERTY
    a). Grant deeds to property I own_____
    b). Trust deeds_____
    c). Notes_____
    d). Mortgages_____
    e). Title Insurance_____
    f). Closing Papers_____
    g). Insurance policies_____
    h). Trust deeds I own_____
    i). Personal notes owed me_____
    j). Leases_____
    k). Bookkeeping records-rent reports_____

7. INSURANCE POLICIES
    a). Life_____
    b). Accident_____
    c). Health and Hospital_____
    d). General_____
    e). Fire_____
    f). Auto_____
    g). Liability_____
    h). Mortgage Life_____

8. HEALTH RECORDS
    a). Personal medical records_____
    b). Disability compensation records_____

9. RETIREMENT RECORDS
    a). Social Security Benefits_____
    b). Medical aid benefits_____
    c). Company retirement and pension papers_____
    d). My retirement plans_____

10.CEMETARY AND BURIAL DATA
    a). Cemetary lot deeds_____
    b). Burial and funeral instructions_____

Plan...

Act...

Grow...

There are only two things to aim at in life; first, to get what you want; and after that, to enjoy it. Only the wisest of mankind achieve the second.

— Logan P. Smith

PLANNING

An intelligent plan is the first step to success. The man who plans knows where he is going, knows what progress he is making and has a pretty good idea when he will arrive. Planning is the open road to your destination. If you do not know where you are going, how can you expect to get there?

—BASIL WALSH

OPPORTUNITY

There is a tide in the affairs of men, which, taken at the flood, leads on to fortune; Omitted, all the voyage of their life is bound in shallows and in miseries. On such a full sea are we now afloat; And we must take the current when it serves, or lose our ventures.

—Shakespeare

You can catch the tide that sweeps men on to success and fortune by planning your actions with the aid of this *SUCCESS PLANNING MANUAL*. Each one of us must do a lot of constructive thinking and create our own pattern for success if we want to reach the high plateaus of achievement that others have accomplished.

2

The First Step Is . . .

DAILY PLANNING

The formula for attainment begins with each individual knowing what he wants. Your first step is to make up your mind. Realize that before you can achieve anything you must have it clearly in your mind. Before you can accomplish anything, you must plan to do it. The builder could not build the building without the plans. Just so, you should have a plan no matter what your objective may be.

These, then, are the two requisites of accomplishment; first, you must make up your mind and know exactly what you want; next, you must have a plan showing how to reach this goal.

★　　★　　★

Make a written plan for each day. This is of primary importance. You will accomplish much more by making a plan in writing and following it out fully and promptly.

Know what you really want. A good plan is to express your desires in concrete form. Commit them to writing. Let them take visible shape before you. You desire health, vitality, wisdom, peace, confidence, courage, hope, friendship, harmony, independence, serenity, cheerfulness, happiness, success, culture, prosperity. Think about these things.

Take time to think and plan carefully and you will make each day more highly productive in actual results. Get a right sense of life's values. Learn to think about essential things first, so that useless trifles will not so easily consume your time. The more earnestly you study right proportion and perspective, the better judgment you will have in planning a well-ordered life.

Get into the habit of living according to plan. Allow yourself a sufficient margin of time in which to do things. Leave nothing to chance. Hurry, worry, and anxiety, defeat your purpose. Eliminate from your life, as far as possible, all undue nervous strain, tension and excitement, and you will accumulate great reserves of mental and physical vitality.

—Grenville Kleiser

One basic principle of organized planning is to do the most important thing first.

THE POWER OF DAILY PLANNING

The most effective way to live reasonably, is every morning to make a plan of one's day, and every night to examine the results obtained.

—Alexis Carrel

PLAN AND PROGRAM yourself. You are the greatest computer ever built. Planning is the only intelligent application of your energy. Remember, that all progress and achievement is planned. It is intelligent, well-planned work that will bring you the rich rewards of life.

How well are *YOU* organizing your life? This is your personal responsibility. No one can eat a meal for you that would give you any strength or nourishment. Just, so, it is your responsibility to: organize yourself, increase your efficiency, develop your full potential, elevate the quality of your life, and live the way you were designed to live.

At the beginning of each day determine what are the really essential things you should do. You'll get more accomplished if you organize your tasks, doing them one at a time in order of their importance.

Charles Schwab, the famous industrialist, says the simple technique of planning his daily schedule helped make one hundred million dollars. Schwab learned the technique from Ivy Lee, the father of modern public relations.

"If you can give me something to alert me to the things I already know I ought to do," Schwab told the famous consultant, "I'll gladly listen to you and pay you anything you ask."

"I can give you something in twenty minutes that will step up your action fifty percent," Lee answered.

Lee handed Schwab a blank piece of paper and said: "Write on this paper the six most important tasks you have to do tomorrow. Number them in the order of their importance. Now put this paper in your pocket and first thing tomorrow morning look at item one and start working on it until it is finished. Then tackle item two in the same way; then item three, and so on. Do this until quitting time. Don't be concerned if you have only finished one or two. Work on the more important ones. The others can wait."

"If you can't finish them all by this method, you couldn't have with any other method either. And without some system, you wouldn't know which was the most important. Do this every working day. After you've convinced yourself of the worth of this system, have your men try it. Try it as long as you wish, and then send me a check for what you think it is worth."

Several weeks later Schwab sent Lee a check for $25,000. The letter that accompanied this amazing sum said that simple lesson in planning was the most profitable procedure Schwab had ever learned.

There are lots of daily, weekly, or monthly schedules available in the stationery stores. Some take the form of a blank calendar. On the opposite page is the weekly form which I have used for over 30 years. A well planned schedule makes time. It keeps you from pondering about what to do next. It sees to it that you are doing the right thing at the right time.

What is a plan? A plan is a method of action, procedure, or arrangement. It is a program to be done. It is a design to carry into effect, an idea, a thought, a project, or a development. Therefore, a plan is a concrete means to help you fulfill your desires.

—Earl Prevette

WEEKLY SCHEDULE

Plans For Week of _____

		MONDAY	TUESDAY	WEDNSDAY	THURSDAY
M	8:00				
O	8:30				
R	9:00				
N	9:30				
I	10:00				
N	10:30				
G	11:00				
	11:30				
	12:00 NOON				
A	1:00				
F	1:30				
T	2:00				
E	2:30				
R	3:00				
N	3:30				
O	4:00				
O	4:30				
N	5:00				
	EVENING				

		FRIDAY	SATURDAY	SUNDAY	NOTES
M	8:00				
O	8:30				
R	9:00				
N	9:30				
I	10:00				
N	10:30				
	11:00				
G	11:30				
	12:00 NOON				
A	1:00				
F	1:30				
T	2:00				
E	2:30				
R	3:00				
N	3:30				
O	4:00				
O	4:30				
N	5:00				
	EVENING				

7

The smug man who does not PLAN goes off the cliff.

PLAN—DON'T GAMBLE on your chances for success! The odds are six to one that most people will be dead broke by the time they reach age 65. Success is achieved through a series of planned actions.

SHORT AND LONG RANGE PLANNING

The fundamental requisite for the success of any plan of life is that it start with the man as he is, and at the time, and in the place and the circumstances, where he is.

By natural temperament, and by the traits and tendencies which have been emphasized in his development, a man is better fitted for certain kinds of work than others. This fact should be taken into consideration in deciding which way to travel.

Certainly, no one would think of building a dwelling house or a business block without first carefully selecting an appropriate and advantageous site and drawing a well considered plan. And in the construction of a life it is no less important to make a wise location, lay the foundations properly, and build by a well considered plan. Few sit down with pen and paper, with expert information and counsel, to plan a working career and deal with the problem of life intelligently as they would deal with the problem of building a house. These are vital problems, and warrant the utmost care and circumspection in their solution.

The lesson biography teaches us is that large success in life has always been achieved only by painstaking effort and preparation. Caesar, we are told, was "ambitious;" Napoleon "schemed;" Foch, "thought and planned;" Stevenson "played the sedulous ape" to his betters; and so forth, and so on. There is nothing hit-or-miss about these phrases. They bespeak careful planning and direction of life.

Benjamin Franklin and Lord Chesterfield, to pick at random two widely separated personalities, have left us records of the minute detail in which they planned their eminent successes. Benjamin Franklin's remarkable career, in particular, is a splendid object lesson of what may be accomplished by the intelligent direction of purpose in life, analyzing this purpose into its constituent elements, outlining the steps to be taken to achieve each of the desired ends, and checking his progress regularly. Essentially, the achiever is the planner.

—Councillor

SEQUENCE OF SUCCESSFUL PLANNING

1. Knowing what you want.

2. Visualizing in detail exactly what you want.

3. Having a great desire.

4. Making up your mind that you are willing to endure the pain of struggle for the comforts, rewards, and the glory that go with achievement.

5. Writing out your plans to obtain your objectives.

6. Taking the necessary steps to accomplish your plans.

7. Having the right mental attitude, the faith and confidence to know that you have the ability to accomplish your goals.

8. Necessary work and perseverance to bring your goals into completion.

9. Accomplishing and enjoying your goals.

This is an established procedure with successful men.

I respect the man who knows what he wishes. The greatest part of all the mischief in the world arises from the fact that men do not sufficiently understand their own aims. They have undertaken to build a tower, and spend no more labor on the foundation than would be necessary to erect a hut.

—Goethe

PLAN AND PROSPER

Modern day living and responsibilities cause you to play a growing role in planning your life. You are constantly taking risks, some big, some small. "Things" don't arrive in the order of their importance. It is up to you to schedule them properly. It is up to you to plan and organize the events that affect your life. Success is achieved through a series of planned actions.

To live successfully one must have definite plans and be aware that there is a limited time in which to get the job done.

Successful careers are motivated by *great desires*. Knowing what we want to accomplish in life, enables us to determine what steps must be taken to take us from where we are to where we want to be.

The wise man bridges this chasm by laying out a long range plan, and many short range plans, for the steps and action that must be taken toward the successful achievement of his purpose or objective. Successful men invariably follow a pattern or formula that leads to success. They develop the habit of conducting their lives by plan or purpose.

A positive mental attitude is a habit of the successful man. He has confidence in his ability to successfully execute and achieve his plans, aims, and objectives.

Plans are powerful! Better planning means better living. One purpose of this Manual is to present as clearly and concisely as possible the fundamental principles, techniques, procedures on which all personal success is based. A man who wants to get somewhere—must have a method, a plan of attack, a program of work.

Put your plans into action. Plans are inert until action infuses them with power. Hard work does not always insure success. Work has to be intelligently and carefully planned, and efficiently organized. You will get more accomplished if you organize your tasks, doing them one at a time in the order of their importance.

Planning is good business. Planning your future is in accord with the soundest principles of mental and physical health. By planning your days and weeks in detail, you put your subconsious mind, with its powerful creative abilities, at work on your problems, even when you are relaxing and sleeping. Even your body doesn't function well when you stop being a goal striver and have nothing to look forward to. Man's success is a result of bringing his dream down to the solid ground of desire, purpose, and decision.

Put your life's plan into determined action and go after what you want with all that's in you.

—Henry J. Kaiser

INVEST IN YOURSELF

You set your destiny by what you make of yourself. Example: A bar of iron is worth $5.00. If made into horseshoes it is worth $10.00. If made into needles it is worth $40.00. If made into balance wheels for watches it is worth $250.00. This is true of another kind of material—YOU.

Success comes from clearly setting up what should be accomplished today, this week, this month. Then compare daily the actual results with the predicted goal. A business under control day-by-day spells a successful year.

STEPS TO PERSONAL PLANNING

Set aside several hours a week for a consultation with yourself and look towards the coming years and the objectives you wish to obtain.

Write down all the things that occur to you. Make a list of the things that you find particularly challenging or stimulating, or that gives you a sense of deep satisfaction.

1. *ASK YOURSELF—"WHAT DO I REALLY WANT TO ACHIEVE, DO, OWN, BECOME?"*

2. *ASK YOURSELF—"DO I HAVE A REAL BURNING DESIRE?"*

3. *ASK YOURSELF—"WHAT ARE THE OBSTACLES?"*

4. *ASK YOURSELF—"WHAT ARE THE REWARDS?"*

5. *ASK YOURSELF—"IS IT WORTH IT?"*

6. *IF YOU DECIDE THE GOAL IS WORTH THE EFFORT*, taste the rewards and get yourself excited about the fruits of your labors.

7. *WHEN YOU DETERMINE YOUR OWN PERSONAL GOALS AND BUSINESS GOALS, ARRANGE YOUR GOALS IN THE ORDER OF THEIR IMPORTANCE.* You may be surprised to find that certain things you set down will not remain on your list after you have finished mulling it over and revising it.

8. *PLAN EXACTLY WHAT ACTION YOU MUST TAKE TO ACHIEVE YOUR GOAL.* What is the first step? What is the second step? What should I do next? Make a list of all the ways you can think of, for reaching your goals.

9. *EVERY PLAN MUST BE IN WRITING.* Written plans are powerful. They direct you toward your goal. A distant goal is the strong medium that keeps enthusiasm strong and ready for the climb.

10. *AFTER YOU HAVE DETERMINED YOUR GOALS*, set a definite time limit. Having exact dates will serve as a powerful subconscious motivational force to keep you in action. Whenever you set up an exact timetable, you then have a standard for reviewing your progress.

Now you are ready to go into action. Fill out the following pages carefully and completely. Then you will be started on a great rewarding experience, "making a life plan." Review your plans often, revising them, bringing them up to date and expanding them.

WHAT LIES BEYOND YOUR HORIZON?

Your ship will not come in unless you have sent one out.

LIST OF MY GOALS

This form serves as a temporary inventory of all your goals. As you read through the rest of this Planning Manual you will see forms which you will use to detail these goals and to organize your steps to achievement in various areas of concern. For now, just write down everything that comes to your mind.

1	
2	
3	
4	
5	
6	
7	
8	
9	
10	
11	
12	
13	
14	
15	
16	
17	
18	
19	
20	
21	
22	

LIST OF MY GOALS

23

24

25

26

27

28

29

30

31

32

33

34

35

36

37

38

39

40

41

42

43

44

45

46

47

48

49

50

GUIDELINES

We suggest that pencil be used for all records subject to change. Use ink for permanent items.

Before filling out your List of Goals you may wish to read the Questionnaire on pages 26 and 27. If you do not have a clear picture of what you want to do, read and answer these questions to yourself each week until you can write down specific answers.

Suggested goals and objectives in planning for each of the eleven areas of your life will be found in each of the sections.

The Questionnaires found in each section are to help you formulate your desires— to stimulate your thinking about what you want out of life.

Determine your goals, then proceed to build a specific plan for each one. Establish definite dates and "hows" of achievement for each objective. Make your plan as complete as possible.

The goal forms—My Plan and My Specific Plan on pages 20 and 21 are similar and are to be used for listing your specific goals and how to take the necessary steps to acquire them. Some may prefer one form over the other, so we have provided both types.

Pages 18 to 25 contain different types of Planning forms. Forms are also provided in the various sections of the Manual and are to be used in the area of your life covered by that section. These areas are:

Goals and aims that have been mere feelings or wishes will begin to formulate themselves in your mind and heart as you work with this Manual. You will be on your way to planning and guiding your life to move toward that which you truly desire for your life.

PLANNING MY LIFE – SHORT RANGE GOALS

What goals do I want to accomplish?	TARGET DATE	*What steps must I take to reach these goals?*
1		
2		
3		
4		
5		
6		
7		
8		
9		
10		

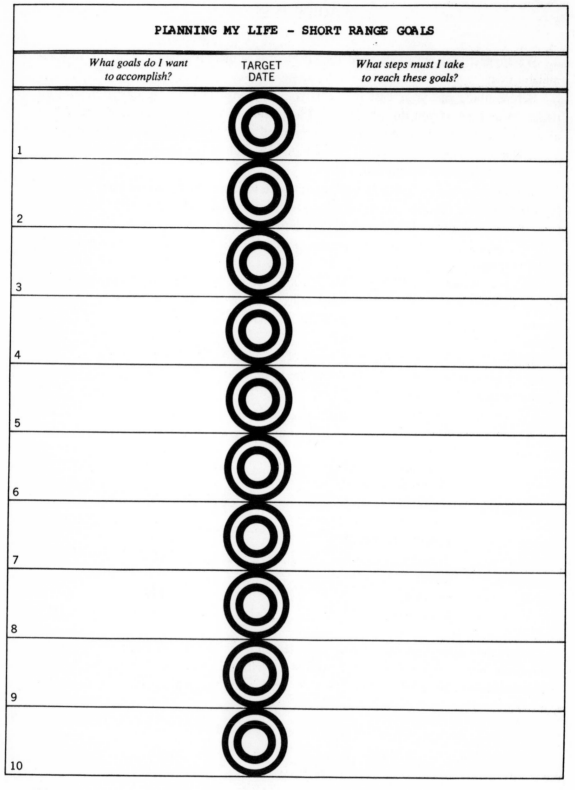

PLANNING MY LIFE – LONG RANGE GOALS

	What goals do I want to accomplish?	TARGET DATE	What steps must I take to reach these goals?
1			
2			
3			
4			
5			
6			
7			
8			
9			
10			

MY PLAN

What do I really want to accomplish? _____
_____
_____
_____
_____
_____

What is the most effective and expedient way of reaching my goal? _____
_____
_____
_____
_____
_____

I have the following abilities, skills, and knowledge for achieving this goal: ____
_____
_____
_____
_____

Additional information, skills, and abilities needed: _____
_____
_____
_____
_____

Here are the places I will go, the people I will see, the sources I will use, to help me gain new knowledge, skills and abilities I need: _____
_____
_____
_____
_____
_____

The first step I will take this week: _____
_____

My next main steps will be as follows (Include deadlines): _____
_____
_____
_____
_____

My target date for reaching this goal: _____

MY SPECIFIC PLAN

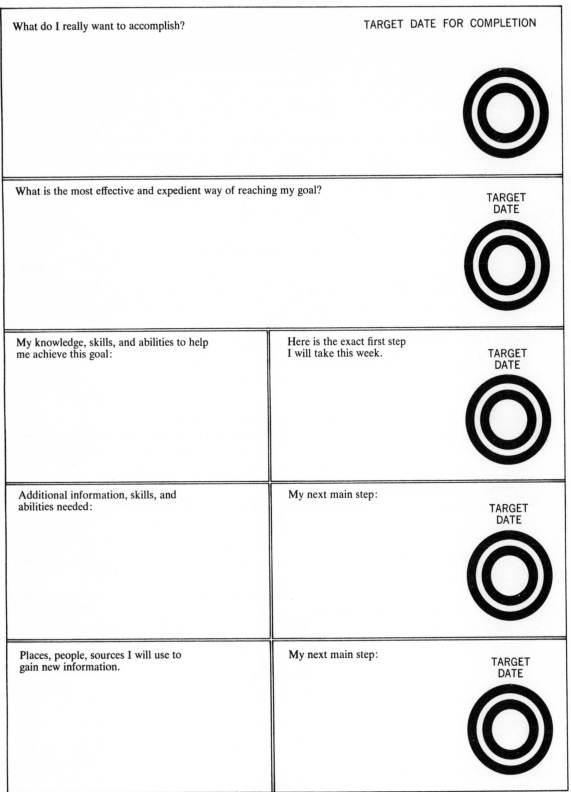

What do I really want to accomplish?

TARGET DATE FOR COMPLETION

What is the most effective and expedient way of reaching my goal?

TARGET
DATE

My knowledge, skills, and abilities to help me achieve this goal:

Here is the exact first step I will take this week.

TARGET
DATE

Additional information, skills, and abilities needed:

My next main step:

TARGET
DATE

Places, people, sources I will use to gain new information.

My next main step:

TARGET
DATE

MY SPECIFIC PLAN

What do I really want to accomplish?	TARGET DATE FOR COMPLETION

What is the most effective and expedient way of reaching my goal?	TARGET DATE

My knowledge, skills, and abilities to help me achieve this goal:	Here is the exact first step I will take this week.	TARGET DATE

Additional information, skills, and abilities needed:	My next main step:	TARGET DATE

Places, people, sources I will use to gain new information.	My next main step:	TARGET DATE

MY SPECIFIC PLAN

What do I really want to accomplish?

TARGET DATE FOR COMPLETION

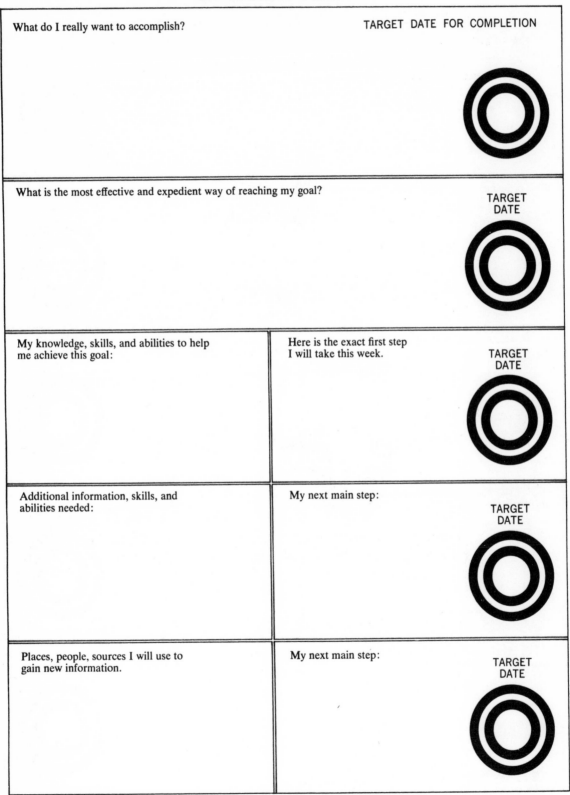

What is the most effective and expedient way of reaching my goal?

TARGET DATE

My knowledge, skills, and abilities to help me achieve this goal:

Here is the exact first step I will take this week.

TARGET DATE

Additional information, skills, and abilities needed:

My next main step:

TARGET DATE

Places, people, sources I will use to gain new information.

My next main step:

TARGET DATE

DREAMS . . .

that tomorrows are made of.

A man is no greater than his dream, his ideal, his hope, and his plan. Man dreams the dream—and fulfilling it, it's the dream that makes the man.

RE-CAP OF IMPORTANT GOALS

FINANCIAL	Target Date		FAMILY AND HOME	Target Date
1		1		
2		2		
3		3		
4		4		
5		5		

PERSONAL	Target Date		TRAVEL AND CULTURE	Target Date
1		1		
2		2		
3		3		
4		4		
5		5		

OCCUPATION-BUSINESS	Target Date		SOCIAL	Target Date
1		1		
2		2		
3		3		
4		4		
5		5		

HEALTH	Target Date		SPIRITUAL	Target Date
1		1		
2		2		
3		3		
4		4		
5		5		

CONSTRUCTIVE THINKING	Target Date		RETIREMENT	Target Date
1		1		
2		2		
3		3		
4		4		
5		5		

MY MOST IMPORTANT GOALS OF ALL	Target Date
1	
2	
3	
4	

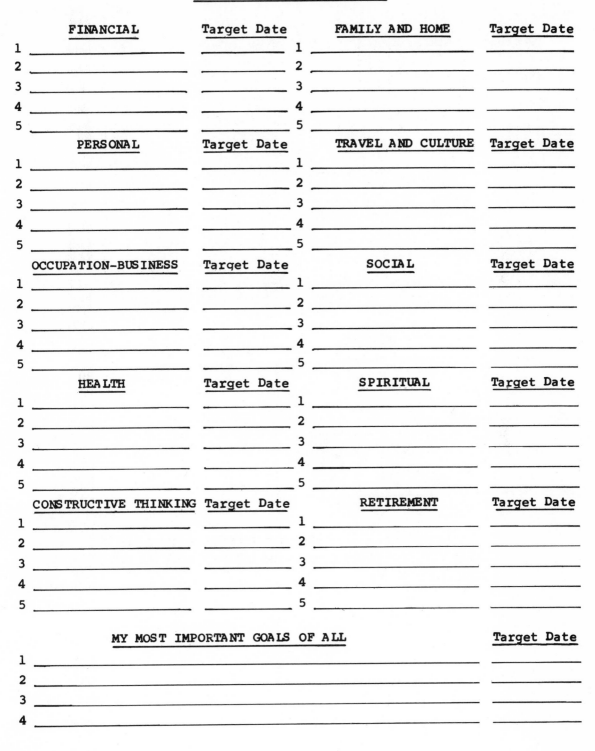

QUESTIONNAIRE

One of the hardest things in the world to discover is one's own aptitude. Ask yourself the following questions:

What is my mission in life?_____
_____
_____
_____
_____
_____

What is my work?_____
_____
_____
_____
_____
_____

What are my talents?_____
_____
_____
_____
_____
_____

What faculties do I possess?_____
_____
_____
_____
_____
_____

What am I best fitted for?_____
_____
_____
_____
_____

What am I doing that is worthwhile?_____
_____
_____
_____
_____

What am I doing that is not worthwhile?_____
_____
_____
_____
_____

QUESTIONNAIRE

In light of the answers to the questionnaire on the previous page
- how will you go about putting your talents and aptitudes to work
for you? What is the best use you can make of your life? Here
are some questions to help you formulate your overall goals.

What will I do with my life?_____
_____
_____
_____
_____

What are my five most important goals in life?_____
_____
_____
_____
_____
_____

What is my one big purpose or objective in life? Detail fully:___
_____
_____
_____
_____
_____

What would I like to accomplish in the next twelve months?_____
_____
_____
_____
_____
_____

What would I like to accomplish in the next five years?_____
_____
_____
_____
_____
_____

What are all the ways I can think of to reach my goals?_____
_____
_____
_____
_____
_____

If I could wave a magic wand and could do, or be, anything I wish-
ed to be, what would I want? (Take into consideration your age,
time needed for training, etc.)_____
_____
_____
_____

PLANNING

He who every morning plans the transactions of the day and follows out that plan carries a thread that will guide him through the labyrinth of the most busy life. The orderly arrangement of his time is like a ray of light which darts itself through all his occupations. But where no plan is laid, where the disposal of time is surrendered merely to the chance of incidents, chaos will soon reign.

—Victor Hugo

24 WAYS TO MOTIVATE YOURSELF
To Your Full Potential

★ Put your plans on paper. Spell out goals and ways to reach them.

★ Be specific. The advice you give yourself must be such that you can put it into practice.

★ Break the job down into small enough pieces so that you have no excuse for not starting it.

★ Establish checkpoints so that you can check your progress.

★ Remind yourself of benefits you expect from completion of the job.

★ Avoid temptation by deliberately avoiding circumstances or thoughts that might sidetrack you.

★ Recognize your limitations. Don't set goals you don't expect to reach.

★ Take advantage of energy peaks, those periods of the day when you are habitually in top form.

★ Take risks. Don't be afraid to try new methods.

★ Use negative motivation. Remind yourself of the unfavorable consequences of inaction.

★ Keep a time-control budget, comparing the priorities of various projects in progress.

★ Set deadlines and hold yourself to them.

★ Make an honest distinction between "I can't" and "I don't want to."

★ Get started. Don't stall.

★ Improve your self-persuasion ability. Learn to know when you are reasoning and when you are rationalizing.

★ Be optimistic, and your chances for success increase.

★ Decide how you want to start, what needs to be done first.

★ Read, especially literature related to your problem.

★ Use self-signaling devices—notes, cues, reminders.

★ Promise yourself rewards—small rewards for small accomplishments, big rewards for big accomplishments.

★ Use the stimulation provided by good news to do extra work.

★ Recognize conflicts and make a choice. Don't let inertia set in.

★ Give yourself the right to make mistakes. No one is perfect.

★ Exercise your sense of humor. Laughter indicates a realistic point of view.

STEPPING STONES TO ACHIEVEMENT

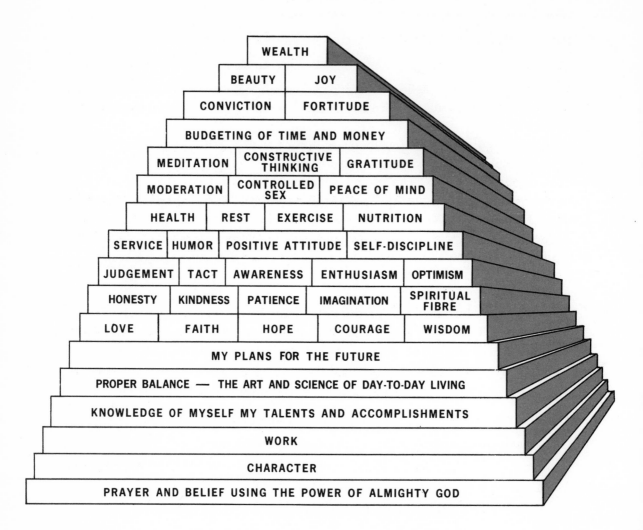

FOUNDATION FOR THE WELL BALANCED LIFE

The highest objective in life is the possession of good character. We say money is power, but character is power in a truer sense. Character is power in a much higher sense than knowledge is power. Character is everything to a MAN.

FOUNDATION FOR THE WELL-BALANCED LIFE

For a well-balanced view of life everyone needs to know . . . what he has yet to do . . . what are his material desires . . . what are his aims for individual self-development . . . and his method for learning the art and science of day-by-day living.

Basically, your inner qualities are your real wealth, not what you have in the bank, or on your financial statement. These qualities represent your intangible wealth. They are what *YOU* are.

The qualities we must continually develop, such as love, faith, joy, beauty, etc., are graphically displayed on the opposite page (30).

This is our real wealth. The success we seek in this Manual is the product of all these qualities, plus our equitable share of the material. This is the real foundation for *BALANCED LIVING,* and a truly successful life.

To some, success is reflected in their financial statement. To others, success is reflected in their children and family. To many, success is reflected in the inner qualities of their lives such as love, kindness, joy, faith, beauty and service. Success means the achievement of anything of value to you.

"When you combine gold and goodness you have the ultimate." When you combine gold and goodness you have reached the high plateau of living. The unbeatable combination that spells SUCCESS with capital letters and underscored. This is the solid foundation for wholesome balanced living.

Honesty, morality, spiritual quality, and the carrying out of high standards and ideals reap the highest rewards and satisfaction in life. Each of us must develop these good qualities if we are to live, be, and have, the best in life. In fact, we should be continually upgrading ourselves throughout our whole lifetime.

Character is the keystone to the good life. Character means the quality of the stuff of which anything is made. Success depends more upon character than upon either intellect or fortune. Your character will be what you yourself choose to make it.

Character is something each one of us must build for himself, out of the laws of God and Nature, the examples of others, and most of all—out of the trials and errors of daily life. Character is the total of thousands of small daily strivings to live up to the best that is in us.

—Lt. Gen. A. G. Trudeau

Life is a great school in which you are constantly learning how better to WORK, PLAN, and ACHIEVE. The schoolmaster of life may seem stern and relentless, but the discipline is for your ultimate good.

—Grenville Kleiser

TECHNIQUES

To Help You Reach Your Goals

VISUALIZING YOUR GOALS

The one most important activity in the forming and consummating of goals is to be able to see yourself clearly in the exact situation you wish to attain. You must be able to create in your mind's eye the exacting particulars and circumstances toward which you aim. These pictures must be of you actually doing the thing. They must be in present tense—as if you already possessed your goal.

Review these mental pictures daily—preferably immediately upon awakening in the morning, and just before sleep at night.

This technique allows you to create within your subconscious mind the actual situation you wish to accomplish. You are in essence telling your mind to put your abilities and body to work to attain this goal. Your subconscious mind knows only the limits which you place on it by conscious thought. It does not distinguish between the real or the imagined. Whatever thoughts you feed into your mind it accepts and acts upon. Learn to use this unique attribute of your subconscious mind to your advantage. You move toward what you dwell upon.

You can also increase your ability to learn more quickly, if you make mental pictures or images of what you are reading, talking about, or studying. See a picture of what you are reading. Picture your goal in your mind. If you can dramatize it in your mind, it must come true. Many people shorten their goal timetable by years, only because of the large vivid pictures in their minds. Through images you can raise your self-concept to the level where you can achieve your goals.

AFFIRM YOUR GOALS

A second step, closely related to visualization, is the affirmation of your goals. An affirmation is a written, positive statement describing the goal you are going to attain. Once you have mastered the ability to actually picture yourself having attained your goal you can then describe that situation in a written affirmation.

Affirmations mean to affirm in the affirmative. That is to state, confidently, in a positive statement, that you already possess your goal. Example: "I am very successful in all that I do. Success comes easily to me."

Now, combine the affirmation and the visualization at the same time. Picture the situation and repeat to yourself out loud your affirmation. Do this every day. After a certain period of time you will begin to feel the confidence and self-assurance you need to attain your goal. You will have dispelled the fear, anxiety and self-doubt which have kept you from possessing the goal in the past.

In addition, in a way we can't explain, you will also find the "way" to reach your goal, for it will work itself out in your mind. You will be releasing a creative power you haven't put to use too often, and you will find yourself developing new ways of attaining things.

SAMPLE AFFIRMATIONS

"I always plan my work. I organize my efforts today for tomorrow, and the future. I work with my goals in mind. I plan ahead to get ahead."

"I eagerly seek to improve myself in every phase of my life."

"I respect myself, and my goals, and I have complete self-assurance in all that I think and do."

"I treat all problems as opportunities to be creative, and as a result, my life is vastly enriched."

"I am easily able to persevere and finish any task I undertake."

"I can bring great concentration to bear upon any subject at anytime."

"I face all my problems with great courage, and thus solve them much more easily."

"I have an unusual ability to reach creative solutions to my problems."

DISPLACING NEGATIVE THOUGHTS

The third step for attaining your goals is to apply the so-called "law of displacement," which is—no two objects can occupy the same space at the same time. This applies to your thoughts as well as to physical things.

The one thing that keeps us from attaining our goals, or even daring to dream of their attainment, is our own negative thoughts. We doubt ourselves. We doubt our ability to execute a specific plan. We doubt our ability to learn new skills, to create new ideas. We keep telling ourselves "I can't."

These are only thoughts—not facts. And because they are only thoughts which we have placed in our minds ourselves, they can be displaced. A negative thought and a positive thought cannot be present in your mind at the same time.

The visualization and affirmation of your goals is the device you use to displace the negative thoughts of doubt, with the positive thoughts of belief. Everytime you have a feeling of doubt or anxiety about attaining your goal displace these thoughts by repeating your affirmations and visualizing that goal. Keep feeding the positive in. After a time you will find the positive thought patterns are dominating your thinking. Continuing this practice you soon have mostly positive thoughts, and there is no room for negative thoughts to enter.

1. State what you want in a positive affirmation.

2. Keep repeating the affirmation until your disbelief changes into belief. It's like dropping (positive) pebbles into a bucket of (negative) water; as illustrated below.

3. By further repetition it will come true. The bucket is filled with (positive) pebbles until all (negative disbelief) water is displaced.

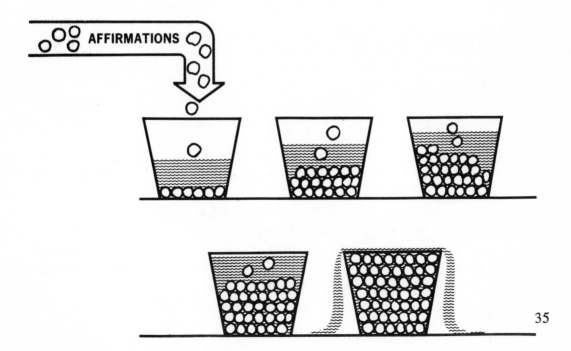

ACTION IS THE BASIS OF ALL ATTAINMENT

Unless you act, all the affirmations, visualization, and thought displacement in the world will not—in themselves—bring your goals into fulfillment. Each day you must *DO SOMETHING* toward their attainment. Look over the steps toward the attainment of your goal which you have written on your Short-Range Goals, and Long-Range Goals forms in the various sections, and on pages 18–19. Each day do something toward each one of them. Nothing succeeds like success. Nothing builds confidence and ability more than successful completion of a task. All great goals, all large tasks, are the result of small every day steps that *YOU* take yourself.

To move from where you are now—to where you want to be: each and every day of your life visualize your goals, affirm your goals, think you *CAN,* and *DO* something toward their attainment. You will find your life broadening, your powers increasing, your whole being developing toward a happier, healthier, and more successful individual.

★　　★　　★

KEYS TO SUCCESS

You

Your success depends upon you.
Your happiness depends upon you.
You have to steer your own course.
You have to shape your own fortune.
You have to educate yourself.
You have to do your own thinking.
You have to live with your own conscience.
Your mind is yours and can be used only by you.
You come into the world alone.
You go to the grave alone.
You are alone with your inner thoughts during the journey between.
You must make your own decisions.
You must abide by the consequences of your acts.
"I cannot make you well unless you make yourself well," an eminent doctor often tells his patients.
You alone can regulate your habits and make or unmake your health.
You alone can assimilate things mental and things material.
Said a Brooklyn preacher, offering his parishioners communion one Sunday: "I cannot give you the blessings and the benefits of this holy feast. You must appropriate them for yourselves. The banquet is spread, help yourself freely.
"You may be invited to a feast where the table is laden with the choicest foods, but

unless you partake of the foods, unless you appropriate and assimilate them, they can do you no good. So it is with this holy feast. You must appropriate its blessings. I cannot infuse them into you."

You have to do your own assimilation all through life.

You may be taught by a teacher, but you have to imbibe the knowledge. He cannot transfuse it into your brain.

You alone can control your mind cells and your brain cells.

You may have spread before you the wisdom of the ages, but unless you assimilate it you derive no benefit from it; no one can force it into your cranium.

You alone can move your own legs.

You alone can use your own arms.

You alone can utilize your own hands.

You alone can control your own muscles.

You must stand on your feet, physically and metaphorically.

You must take your own steps.

Your parents cannot enter into your skin, take control of your mental and physical machinery, and make something of you.

You cannot fight your son's battles; that he must do for himself.

You have to be captain of your own destiny.

You have to see through your own eyes.

You have to use your own ears.

You have to master your own faculties.

You have to solve your own problems.

You have to form your own ideals.

You have to create your own ideas.

You must choose your own speech.

You must govern your own tongue.

Your real life is your thoughts.

Your thoughts are of your own making.

Your character is your own handiwork.

You alone can select the materials that go into it.

You alone can reject what is not fit to go into it.

You are the creator of your own personality.

You can be disgraced by no man's hand but your own.

You can be elevated and sustained by no man save yourself.

You have to write your own record.

You have to build your own monument—or dig your own pit.

Which are you doing?

— B. C. Forbes

"I banked in Switzerland and forgot the number of my secret account."

Section Two

FINANCIAL

Money Management

If wisely used, money may do much. Gold is power. Money gives us the means of acquiring what we wish. If fresh air, a good house, books, music, etc. are enjoyable, money will buy them; if leisure is an advantage, money enables us to take it; if seeing the world is delightful, it will pay for our journeys; if to help our friends, to relieve those who are in distress is a privilege, money confers on us this great blessing.

—John Lubbock

Money is the foundation of all successful business.
Learn to enjoy the money you make.

MONEY: ITS USE AND ABUSE

Money is probably the biggest problem to the majority of people in our country. The money problem is generally caused by poor management. With every dollar you make, you have a choice on where to put it. When you make that choice you eliminate 99 other places you could have put it. That is why you need to plan. Good sound money management is your defense against money problems.

The day is rapidly approaching when practically all homes will be mortgaged. This is fast becoming an American way of life for we are used to luxury living and many times we are spending beyond our means. It is said that 80% of the automobiles on the streets are financed.

Many people are not aware that money causes the biggest percentage of family separation and family break-ups and divorces. Many people do not realize the vicious part financial trouble is playing in destroying the American home.

Much of our sickness arises from emotional and nervous disorders. And a large percent of illness is caused by money worries and economic insecurity. Physical, financial, and mental health are closely allied.

The number of consumer bankruptcies today is even greater than in the great depression of the nineteen thirties. Installment debts are the leading cause. A state of debt is normal today, for most of us, and continuous. Easy credit has become a characteristic feature of our time.

Individuals who do not plan as they should, usually, find that their finances are run on a hit or miss basis. It is not hard to see that careful financial planning would do the individual or the family a world of good.

Many older men, even businessmen, do not always run their family affairs on a businesslike basis. They may be top administrators at the office but they often are loose with their personal and family budget.

Countless people feel the need for expert guidance and for effective ways of handling their money. They flounder because they do not know where to turn for expert guidance in money management.

A purposeful savings and investment program can be a powerful aid in improving your standard of living and in reaching your desired goals. It takes money for just about everything concerning life and living. Money is the very lifeblood of business.

Always keep accounts, and keep them carefully. Keep them so that you know how the money goes and how much things cost you. No man who knows what his income is, and what he is spending, will run into extravagance. Spendthrifts begin by shutting their eyes to what they are doing. No one would face the precipice of ruin with his eyes open. Whatever you do then, live within your income. Save something, however little, every month.

—John Lubbock

THE FOUR AREAS OF GOOD MONEY MANAGEMENT

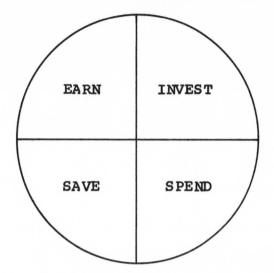

Money management boils down to, how to *EARN, INVEST, SAVE,* and *SPEND* money. Four separate important facets, and each affects the other. It sounds simple, but it requires planning, discipline, and all the other ingredients which make up good money management.

I would say that the place where most of us fail, is in saving money. We spend money without planning and disciplining ourselves. We are continually and habitually overspending. I believe most people concentrate on earning and investing money and neglect the importance of saving and lack wise planning and discipline in spending of their hard earned money.

All four areas are important. In order to keep in good financial health, realize that careful attention must be given to each specific area. About half the expenses of life are entirely outside the actual necessities of life.

Everybody can't be as rich as Paul Getty, but you can improve your own present financial position. You do this simply by realizing you need perspective on your money management. The four basic groupings are: Your income—your investments—your ability to save—your careful spending.

By carefully and continually going over all your records you should be able to adjust your outgo in relation to income and build up a surplus. Once you have a surplus or savings you can invest these dollars to work for you.

On the following pages you will find a comprehensive discussion of each one of the four areas with pertinent forms to help you organize and plan for good money management.

Financial success in the highest sense is not so much making money as it is making a wise use of money.

What have you done in your productive life in order to take care of yourself when you are unable to work? (Non-productive years)

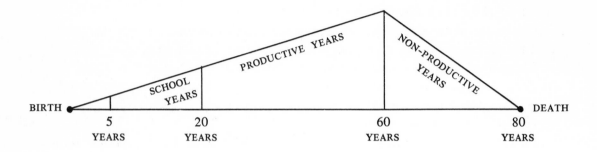

Intelligent planning during the span of your lifetime will help you increase the quality of your life and bring you personal success and fortune.

One goal of every man should be to accumulate enough money so that as early as possible in his life, he can buy some leisure time and do the things he has always wanted to do, to serve others and enjoy life to the fullest.

44

MONEY MANAGEMENT

We are living in a world where we must have money. Managing money is the art of compelling dollars to work for us after we have worked for them. Money makes money. Hundreds of men and women double and triple their incomes by making sound financial plans.

We earn and spend lots of money. During our lifetime practically each one of us will earn and spend over $350,000.

One of the prime objectives with money is to save a little each month and put it to work for us. Small savings, if properly handled, can grow into a fortune over the years.

The proper handling of money requires time and attention, otherwise it goes down the drain. You have to set up a budget to control it and keep studying and revising it to improve your financial position. Properly managing your money takes skill. Know where it goes and control its flow.

First, let's examine a business. It succeeds or fails on its profit or losses and on that basis alone. At the beginning of each year it estimates its gross income, expenses and net profits, and then plans on how to use the profit most effectively. Month by month the businessman compares his accomplishments with his forecast. If he is doing better than anticipated he may expand; if worse he may have to cut back and sometimes set a new course, but at all times he knows where he is and what goals he is aiming for.

Do you have a money management system? How to finance not only day to day needs but also future aims and desires, should be the objective of every man, in every income group, in every circumstance.

The first goal of a value minded spending plan should be accelerated repayment of debts. There is little financial value in building up savings which may earn four to five percent interest for you while you still owe installment debts and loans on which you pay true interest rates of 12 to 22 percent, and sometimes more. Plan to get on a cash basis as soon as you can.

The second goal is to establish a capital reserve fund. As soon as you have repaid all debts you should start building a capital reserve fund. This is really a separate savings fund used over and over to take advantage of reduced price opportunities and help finance purchases on a cash basis instead of the costly installment basis. Your capital reserve fund is also a necessary provision for crisis. Things happen fast in life, be prepared for all emergencies.

YOUR PERSONAL FINANCIAL RECORDS

First, fill out the financial sheet in pencil, take stock of your finances, see what your net worth is. Twice a year revise your financial statement pages 47 and 48. This is a typical financial report you will fill out when applying for a bank loan.

In one column you list the present-day value of all the things you own.

In the second column you list the amounts you owe and add them together.

Then you subtract what you owe from what you own. What is left is your *net worth*.

A steady increase in your net worth each year is a worthy goal.

Keep asking yourself:—"What investments can I make, or what savings can I make, or what can I do, to have a greater net worth one year from now?"

1. Do you have a plan how you will pay off your debts?
2. Do you have a savings program?
3. Do you have an investment program?
4. Are your investments diversified?
5. Make out a realistic budget for this year.
6. What do you estimate your cash income for this year?
7. What do you estimate your cash outgo for this year?
8. What do you estimate your surplus?
9. Make this year a turning point in your life.

*May the sun
always shine on me.*

FINANCIAL STATEMENT

PLEASE COMPLETE IN DETAIL:

Name_____ Customer At _____ Br.

Address_____ Occupation _____

Financial Condition As Of _____ 19____

ASSETS	Amount			LIABILITIES	Amount		
Cash in Bank	$			Notes Payable to Bank	$		
Cash in Other Banks (Detail)				Notes Payable to Other Banks (Detail)			
Accounts Receivable—Good				Accounts Payable			
Notes Receivable—Good (Detail)				Notes Payable to Others (Detail)			
Due from Relatives				Income Tax Payable			
Listed Stocks and Bonds (Itemize on Reverse)				Unpaid Taxes & Interest			
Unlisted Stocks and Bonds (" " ")							
Real Estate and Buildings (" " ")				Mortgages or Liens on Real Estate			
Mortgages and Trust Deeds (" " ")				(Itemize on Reverse)			
Cash Value Life Insurance				Loans on Life Insurance			
Automobiles, etc.				Installment Contracts & Chattel Mortgages			
Personal Property							
Other Assets (Detail)				Other Liabilities (Detail)			
				Total Liabilities	$		
				NET WORTH	$		
Total	$			Total	$		

ANNUAL INCOME		ANNUAL EXPENDITURES	
Salary	$	Property Taxes and Assessments	$
Securities	$	Federal and State Income Taxes	$
Rentals—Gross	$	Mortgage Payments and Interest	$
Business	$	Other Contract Payments	$
Otherwise	$	Insurance	$
		Living Expenses	$
TOTAL INCOME	$	TOTAL EXPENDITURES	$

Life Insurance $_____ Payable to_____ In which Companies?_____

Auto Liability Insurance?_____ Have you ever been in Bankruptcy?_____

What Contingent Liabilities? (Endorsements, Surety, Judgments, Suits)_____

I hereby certify the above statement, including the reverse side, to be true and correct to the best of my knowledge and belief.

Date Signed_____, 19____ (Sign here)_____

47

REAL ESTATE——Title stands in name of:

Legal Description, Street Address and Type of Improvements	Value of Property	Amount of Encumbrance	Encumbrance Owing To	How Payable	Gross Rental Income
Total	$	$			

Has Homestead been declared?   Insurance Coverage?

STOCKS & BONDS——Standing in name of:

Number of Shares or Face Value of Bonds	Description	Where Listed	Present Market Value	Amount Pledged
	Total		$	

MORTGAGES & TRUST DEEDS OWNED——Standing in name of:

Name of Payor	Street Address and Type of Improvements	Unpaid Balance	How Payable	1st or 2nd Lien	Value of Property
	Total	$			

REFERENCES:

INCOME

Everyone of us wants to make more money than we are making right now. Next year we want to earn more than we are this year. The way we can get more from year to year is to *PLAN* a program of earnings.

Our major source of earning in our lifetime is our job, profession, or business and we must therefore plan within the realm of the job we now hold. How can we better our performance, or knowledge, so that we will be worth more to those who pay for our services? To earn more we must produce more.

Income planning should be based upon the earnings you have now from your present job or profession. How much income you have has nothing to do with how well you manage it. Even the wealthiest people must make choices about what to do with their fortunes because no one has unlimited finances.

To put money to the best use possible you must: 1. Know how much you earn each year; 2. Know how much it costs you to live; 3. Know how much you have left over after necessities; 4. Plan what you will do with the remainder. It is what you do with the surplus that makes or breaks you. Millions are made from investments, interest, equities, not from wages.

The ideal situation is to plan and grow until you obtain a diversified income: 1. Income from occupation (wages); 2. Income from income property (rent); 3. Income from stock investment (dividends); 4. Income from miscellaneous sources.

Use the forms provided in this Financial Section to determine your income, your expenses, and the areas where you can save and invest your money so that you do earn more each year.

A lot of us are fooled into thinking "Oh, if I just had $5000 more a year my troubles would be over." That is not true. If you do not manage properly what you have now, no amount of increase is going to improve your situation.

So the key is not always more money, but more planning. Start planning the wise use of your present income in order to gain the goals you desire. Money is for use. If it doesn't get you what you want in life you are wasting it.

Motivate yourself to better money management by clearly defining the goals you want to accomplish in life. Most of them will require money somewhere along the line. Then plot your earnings, savings, investing, and spending in order to reach your goals.

You have to go out on a limb occasionally, for that is where the fruit is.
—Frank Scully

INCOME

An Income Is Just About The Most Important Material Thing In Life!

WHAT HOLDS THE CIRCLE UP? INCOME, OF COURSE!

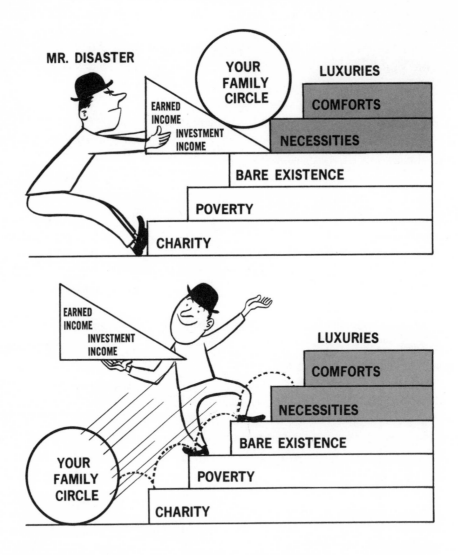

When earning power is cut off by some crisis, sickness or accident, the wheel, which represents your family circle, rolls down the steps unless something holds it up. What holds the circle up? *INCOME, OF COURSE!*

HERE IS HOW I GET MY INCOME

This form tells you <u>where</u> your money is coming from, and <u>when</u> it is coming. Estimate the year's income as far as possible. Extra earnings such as commissions, rents, etc. can be estimated on the basis of past earnings.

Source	Jan	Feb	Mar	Apr	May	Jun	Jul	Aug	Sep	Oct	Nov	Dec
Salary												
Commission												
Business												
Rents												
Dividends												
Interest												
" Notes												
" Bonds												
" Banks												
Trading												
Profits												
Gifts												
Bonus												
Tips												
Other												
Pension												
Social												
Security												
TOTAL FOR MO.												

ANNUAL SUMMARY

Source	Years Total	% of Total	Projections - Plans

It is not what comes into a man's hands that enriches him, but what he saves from slipping through them. The saving habit grows rapidly, and your money grows rapidly, with it. Your procedure should be as follows: (a) determine positively that you will save; (b) keep an accurate cash account; (c) open a savings bank account; (d) deposit a sum regularly; (e) deposit extra and unexpected receipts.

—Grenville Kleiser

SAVINGS

The most important reason for saving money is the accumulation of working capital. *You do not become wealthy on the money you work for*. It is the *money that works for you* that makes the difference.

Do you have a savings program?

The habit of saving money should be followed on a percentage basis, by setting aside a definite percent of all income to be saved. When the savings fund is large enough it should be put to work in some kind of safe investment, where it will begin to multiply itself. It should not be used for current expenses, nor should it be used for emergencies as long as they can be handled by other means.

The best way to save money is to do without something you want. You can satisfy a man's needs but never his wants. It is unbelievable how many men who are so astute about making money, can often be so lax about saving it.

Here are a few suggested savings, you may have many of your own suggestions:

1. Pay NOW and SAVE now. Eliminate interest wherever possible.
2. If you must borrow, watch your interest rate. Never pay too much for money.
3. Do not over buy and do not buy things you can do without.
4. Try and reduce the cost of the goods and services you purchase by shopping around.
5. "Spend and save." Advertising slogans tell us we must spend in order to save. Saving and spending, however, are exact opposites.

The formula for making you a success with your money:

1. Have a plan to earn money.
2. Have a plan to save money.
3. Have a plan to invest money.
4. Have a plan to carefully spend your money.

Each of the above is dependent upon the other for success. If they are working together in concert—like a majestic orchestra—they will bring harmony and joy into your financial life. The financial part of life is mainly the cause of all the discord, heartaches, and trouble.

You will be smiling all the way to the bank—for you will be going there as a depositor, not as a borrower.

Economy is in itself a source of great revenue.—Seneca

Overdrawn . . . I'm sure the bank made a mistake, dear!

I believe that THRIFT is essential to well-ordered living and that economy is a prime requisite of a sound financial structure, whether in government, business, or personal affairs.

—John D. Rockefeller, Jr.

BANK ACCOUNTS

Name of Bank:
Address:
Account Number:
Location of Bank Books:

Month	Balance	Deposits This Mo.	Income Source	Interest Received	Withdrawn This Mo.	Remarks
Jan						
Feb						
Mar						
Apr						
May						
Jun						
Jul						
Aug						
Sep						
Oct						
Nov						
Dec						

How long will it take to double your money? to find out
divide the interest rate into 72. The answer is the number of years. Example: money invested at 6% interest
compounded annually will double in (6 into 72) 12 years.

Name of Bank:
Address:
Account Number:
Location of Bank Books:

Month	Balance	Deposits This Mo.	Income Source	Interest Received	Withdrawn This Mo.	Remarks
Jan						
Feb						
Mar						
Apr						
May						
Jun						
Jul						
Aug						
Sep						
Oct						
Nov						
Dec						

SAVINGS AND INVESTMENT PROGRAM

(For assets yielding interest or dividends, also see Pg.59-63)

CASH THRIFT ACCOUNTS
(Savings & Loan Assoc. Banks, Credit Unions)

Institution	Dollar Amount	Current Yield
1._____	$_____	_____
2._____	$_____	_____
3._____	$_____	_____
4._____	$_____	_____
5._____	$_____	_____
6._____	$_____	_____
7._____	$_____	_____
8._____	$_____	_____
TOTAL...............$_____		

BONDS-GOVERNMENT, CORPORATE

Kind or Name	Dollars Invested	Market Value	Interest Rate
1._____	$_____	$_____	_____%
2._____	$_____	$_____	_____%
3._____	$_____	$_____	_____%
4._____	$_____	$_____	_____%
5._____	$_____	$_____	_____%
6._____	$_____	$_____	_____%
TOTAL...............$_____			

MUTUAL FUNDS

Name of Fund	# Shrs.	Dollars Invested	Market Value	Current Divident
1._____	_____	$_____	$_____	_____%
2._____	_____	$_____	$_____	_____%
3._____	_____	$_____	$_____	_____%
4._____	_____	$_____	$_____	_____%
5._____	_____	$_____	$_____	_____%
TOTAL...............$_____				

56

INVESTMENTS

Putting Your Money To Work For You

In all phases of life, the successful people are those who do what they know best. Apply this to your own position. Always remember to stay with what you know best. Own a goose that lays golden eggs—*build a diversified investment portfolio.*

There are so many kinds of investments a person can make that we will not list them all here. The most common investments are stocks and bonds, and real estate.

COMMON STOCKS have an advantage over real estate in that they are more liquid and can be bought and sold more readily. They do not require the management which income real estate property does. Stocks are an easier way of life. However, the dividends could be cut off in an extreme emergency.

REAL ESTATE: The biggest advantage in owning income property is the ability to take depreciation. Real estate income property gives you more spendable money, as the allowable depreciation is charged against ordinary income, and your tax is paid on a long term capital investment when you sell the property. However, you cannot always sell real estate readily. Sometimes it takes months to sell.

TRUST DEEDS and mortages have the advantage of no management, minimum attention. They are less trouble than operating income property. The annual yield from first trust deeds is usually determined in the market. Second or successive trust deeds should show a substantial increase in interest as well as possible discount commensurate with risk. Disadvantages: No depreciation, no appreciation, legal costs and trouble to take possession of property in case of default.

SAFETY: The first sound principle of investment is security for your capital. It is not wise to be intrigued by larger earnings when the principal may be lost. Guard your treasure from loss by investing only where your capital is safe, where it may be reclaimed if desirable, and where you will not fail to collect a fair rental. There is free cheese in every trap. Secure the advice of the experienced in the profitable handling of your money.

When you are young make all the money you can and invest it so you will have the capital which will keep you in your later years. When you are young you should be "capital building," "estate building," so that as you become older you will be receiving a monthly spendable income from your investments.

Unless you are young do not invest in some long term gain that you will not be around to enjoy. When you are older your primary financial need is a good "monthly spendable" income from your investments.

A cardinal rule before making an investment is: write down all the advantages and disadvantages. Write out all the questions you can think of. How much money is required? How much does it earn? What is the appreciation factor? What is the safety factor? What is the liquidity value? What is the collateral value? Write out all the answers to the questions. Write down on paper everything you can think of regarding the investment. When applicable see the experts before making any decisions.

INSURANCE: How much should I invest in insurance? Insurance boils down to one thing, and one thing only—money. Here for example are some of the ways you can use life insurance in your financial planning—

★ To dovetail your personal retirement program with the money you'll get from Social Security or a company pension.

★ To help finance the college expenses of your children, or provide a "dowry" for your daughter when she marries.

★ To pay off money you owe on your house, your car or your household goods in case of your death or disability.

★ To guarantee against the loss of a family business in case of your death, or to protect a partnership or other business enterprise in case one of the key men dies.

★ To provide cash for estate-settlement costs, and to help cut taxes on your estate.

Insurance is recognized by some as the keystone to a man's whole savings and retirement program, as a way he can build an estate and pass it along to his heirs.

We must plan carefully how to invest: to get the most return, to make our investments keep ahead of inflationary trends, and to use the proper means which are available to keep our taxes at a minimum. Always consider the increase in the cost of living, which has consistently gone up each year.

Write out and plan how you can improve your investment portfolio and your own affairs, and make this the most prosperous year of your life.

No one can retire successfully without financial security. Financial security is one of the most important phases of your life. You need money to buy time, food and raiment, books, hobbies, travel, etc.

To get profit without risk, experience without danger, reward without work, is as impossible as it is to live without being born.

—A. P. Gouthey

LIST OF STOCKS I OWN

The purpose of this form is to inventory the stock you own and its current market value.

Date	Stock	Number of Shares	Cost Price	Comm.	Total Invested	Market Quotation		
						Date	Amt.	+Gain -Loss

STOCK CERTIFICATE NUMBERS

Stock certificates, if lost, take several months to a year to replace even if registered in your name. Keep a list of all your stock certificate numbers.

Name	Number	Name	Number

LIST OF REAL ESTATE I OWN

Income Property and
Unimproved Property

* INCOME PROPERTY *

Description Address - Units	Gross Income	Years Expense	Net Income	Prin. Pymt.	Net. Spend. $	%	Market Value

*   UNIMPROVED PROPERTY AND NON-INCOME PROPERTY   *

Description	Cost	Years Interest	Years Taxes	Years Upkeep	Total $ Invested	Market Value

Borrower's Name	Collateral: Discription Value	Amount of Note	Payable			Balance Due
			Date	Int.	Prin.	

LIST OF INSURANCE I OWN

LIFE INSURANCE

Issue Date	Age Issued	Type	Company	Policy Number	Face Amount	Premium

GENERAL INSURANCE

Type	Issue Date	Date Expires	Company	Policy Number	Face Amount	Premium

CHARGE IT!

The secret to making money is saving it. It is not what a man earns, not the amount of his income, but the relation of his spending to his income that determines his poverty or wealth.

—Colton

SPENDING

How Much Should You Spend On What?

Before buying anything it is well to ask whether one could not do without it.

—John Lubbock

The course you take will be your own decision, for when it comes to spending, you, like the rest of us, have many complicated problems and you make the decision, you take the responsibility.

Today the American consumer is in a sea of debt. He is struggling to keep afloat and solvent. The modern installment plan of buying, while it is undeniably a great convenience, is also a great hazard, for it leads to the purchase of many articles one could quite well get along without. No purchase should ever be made of anything on the installment plan without governing the purchase by a strict budget system. A majority of the people will buy almost anything that is offered them as long as they can get it on easy payment terms. They do not realize that enough of these "easy" payments will soon exceed their ability to pay.

Frugality is one of the essentials of success. The habit of planned savings encourages frugality; makes it an established habit. If one is careless in his habits of spending money he will more than likely be careless in many other important matters where carelessness will be fatal to his chances for success.

One cardinal principle for careful spending is to realize the income level of your earnings and then to live on a lower level. Learn to happily do without in order to save and invest so as to build a substantial estate for the future.

Are you an impulsive buyer? Make this test before every purchase:

1. Do I really need it?
2. What will happen if I don't buy it?
3. Am I buying it to hurt someone?
4. Am I buying it to impress someone?
5. Am I buying it to prove something?
6. What will I give up if I buy it?
7. Who will benefit?
8. How will I pay for it?
9. Does it fit my budget?
10. Does this spending fit in with my overall goals and ambitions?

"Caveat Emptor"—let the buyer beware—is an old business maxim. And the buyer must indeed beware, for who is interested in his welfare except himself?

FIXED EXPENSES AND SAVINGS

Fixed expenses are big expenses such as taxes, insurance which occur regularly. Good money management provides an amount to be set aside each month to pay for these items when they are due. Savings and rainy day funds are necessary to keep you ahead when emergencies arise, and to provide for a better future.

Fixed Expense	Jan	Feb	Mar	Apr	May	Jun	Jul	Aug	Sep	Oct	Nov	Dec
TAXES:												
Fed.Inc.												
State "												
Property												
Other												
DEBTS:												
Mortgage												
Bank Loan												
FinanceCo												
Dept store												
Other												
INSURANCE:												
Life												
Health												
Auto												
Homeowner												
Other												
SAVINGS:												
Bonds												
Investmt												
Sav.Acct.												
Other												
RAINY DAY												
VACATION												
Monthly Total												

HOW MUCH I HAVE AVAILABLE FOR DAY TO DAY EXPENSES

	Jan	Feb	Mar	Apr	May	Jun	Jul	Aug	Sep	Oct	Nov	Dec
Monthly Income (pg 51)												
Fixed Payments (Pg 66)												
DIFFERENCE												

This is what you have left to meet your day-to-day expenses each month. Allot this amount on the form below.

DAY TO DAY EXPENSES

Estimate daily expenses for the first month or two. Then keep exact records and adjust your allotments realistically after you know what you really spend. If you can't meet your daily expenses as they are, some planning and stricter budgeting will be necessary.

I will Spend On:	Jan	Feb	Mar	Apr	May	Jun	Jul	Aug	Sep	Oct	Nov	Dec
Food												
House:												
−Utilities												
−Furniture												
−Repairs												
Medical												
Clothes												
Automobile												
Transport.												
Personal												
Allowances												
Donations												
Gifts												
Education												
TOTAL												

A person is rich in proportion to the number of things which one can afford to let alone.

Your money's only as good as what you do with it.
                                              —J. Paul Getty

BUDGET

The way you budget your lifetime earnings determines the kind of life you will have.

The old fashioned way of making a budget was to provide first for the necessities, such as rent, food, clothing, light, heat. If any money was left in the budget it would go towards the luxuries such as a new car, vacation, air conditioner, dishwasher, color TV.

However, today, the beautiful and persuasive advertising has convinced people that if they don't have all the wonderful goods and services shown in the full-color ads in magazines and television, they are not sharing in the American way of life.

How many can really afford a swimming pool, four weeks vacation, domestic help, two cars, electric organ, electric dishwasher, electric garage doors, air conditioning, color TV, etc., plus all the service expense that goes along with them?

Budget your expenses and do not include money for luxuries such as jewelry, statues, fancy cars, fancy clothes, fancy foods, things quickly gone and forgotten, anything extravagant. The money here is not *working for you*.

Your budget will allow you to save money to invest in items which are income producing such as savings accounts, income property, stocks, trust deeds, or other income producing investments. This money will be working for you, and you will become highly gratified and accumulate substantial worth.

Family money is hard to manage because a family is subject to so many emotional demands. Standards become "what everyone else is doing." In the business world money is managed by experts who take a long hard cold look before spending.

No family can afford to be without a working budget, and the simpler you can keep it the better. Everyone needs practical guidelines for spending and saving.

The purpose of a budget is to help fatten your purse. It is to assist you in having the necessities, and, in so far as attainable, your other desires. It is to enable you to realize your most cherished desires by defending them from casual wishes.

Like a bright light in a dark cave your budget shows up the leaks from your purse. This enables you to stop the leaks and control your expenses for definite and gratifying purposes.

People are usually at a loss to explain what has happened to all the money they have handled. They are generally amazed when they investigate further and discover that much of it has gone for things they really never needed and which did not help them achieve any major goals in life.

Sir, I want to fight the War on Poverty . . . I need some ammunition!

BORROWING AND LENDING

Practically every man will borrow money sooner or later. The smart man will get money at the least cost.

What does it cost to borrow on life insurance? Much less than you have to pay for most other loans. This is because life insurance loans are secured by the world's best collateral—money you already own.

What does it cost to borrow money using your stock as collateral? The bank will loan you up to 70% of the market value of the stock and you will still receive the dividends. The interest rate will be good, as the bank practically has cash security for their loan.

Before you borrow, plan out how you will repay the loan. The better your collateral the lower should be the cost of the loan. Read the contract carefully. Figure out the full cost of the money you are borrowing. Can you pay it off earlier without a penalty?

There is nothing wrong about owing money as long as you are able to make the payments when they are due. Installment buying is also part of modern living. It enables us to enjoy the good things of life as we pay for them. The secret is to keep the amount of the installments down to a sensible share of your income. High interest rate means bad security.

Your debts, are they too high? Plan to get on a cash basis, cut off the necklace of millstones around your neck. Some people are walking a tightrope all their lives, a few are doing it with a peg leg.

LENDING

Borrowing and lending is the business of your bank. If you lend always obtain ample collateral or security. If you don't know a person well enough to borrow money from him, don't lend him any. Govern your loans by what you can afford to lose.

Don't worry if you borrow, only if you lend.—Russian Proverb

He that is surety for a stranger shall smart for it; but he that hateth suretyship is sure.

—Proverbs

Neither a borrower nor a lender be,
For loan oft loses both itself and friend,
And borrowing dulls the edge of husbandry.
—Shakespeare

MONEY I OWE					
Payable to:	Address	Collat-eral	Face Amount	Interest Payable	Payments Due Amount

FAMILY AND PERSONAL LOANS DUE ME

Name of Borrower	Amount Loaned	Payable			Balance Due Me	Security
		Date	Int.	Prin.		

FINANCIAL QUESTIONNAIRE

Everyone is interested in the proper and profitable use of money, which comes from two sources - EARNED INCOME and INVESTMENT INCOME. What does financial independence mean to you? Analyze your financial position to determine how close you are to financial security. What plans can you make in the struggle to earn more, to save and invest prudently, and to have success with your money?_____
_____
_____
_____
_____

Describe your present financial condition. Do you have a budget, are you living within your income? Do you have enough after expenses to save and invest? Do you have good control over your spending?_____
_____
_____
_____

Do you really want financial success? Do you want to pay the price of long hours, sacrifice, specialized training, the constant battle that is business?_____
_____

Would you choose rather to operate on a nominal level, whatever your particular profession pays, live within your income, and just enjoy things as you go along?_____
_____
_____

Do you have a systematic savings program? If not, how can you get started?_____

What type of investments do you know the most about? What kind of investments fit into your present income?_____
_____

Do you have diversified investments?_____

Does your present investment portfolio give you a substantial monthly income?_____

Do you have part of your assets invested in inflation-resistant things such as real estate or good common stocks?_____
_____

What kind of investment program do you want - that suits your present money and time budget? Remember, after-tax dollars determines our financial position, present and future, as individuals, families, and corporations._____
_____
_____

Do you have a diversified investment portfolio? Are you in the
process of building one? Describe. _____
_____
_____
_____
_____

At what age would you like to retire? _____
_____

After you retire, how much per year will it cost you and your
dependents to live? _____
_____
_____
_____

Do you expect to do any work after you retire? _____
_____

How much capital do you think you should accumulate so that, when
you retire you can live comfortably on the income from it?
  (Remember, it would require $100,000 in savings at 5% yield
   to produce a yearly income of $5000.) _____
_____
_____
_____

Write out your complete plans for your personal financial future.
_____
_____
_____
_____
_____
_____
_____

Today it isn't a question of whether you want to invest or not.
You **must** **invest**. Money is decreasing in value. By investing you
participate in the growth of the economy, and you protect the pur-
chasing power of your life-time savings from deteriorating further
through continued inflation.

SUGGESTED GOALS AND OBJECTIVES
FOR YOUR FINANCIAL PLANS

Get into a good cash position.
Build investment portfolio.
Stock interest in company that
  I work for.
Program to pay off loans.
Increased income.
Better use of planned income.
Savings program.
Stock and bond investment.
Real Estate investment.

Income property investment.
Trust deeds investment.
Supplementary income.
Income from hobbies.
Insurance - annuities - life.
Development of new ideas.
Educational fund.
Retirement fund.
Church, educational or char-
  ity donations.

MY FINANCIAL LIFE – SHORT RANGE GOALS

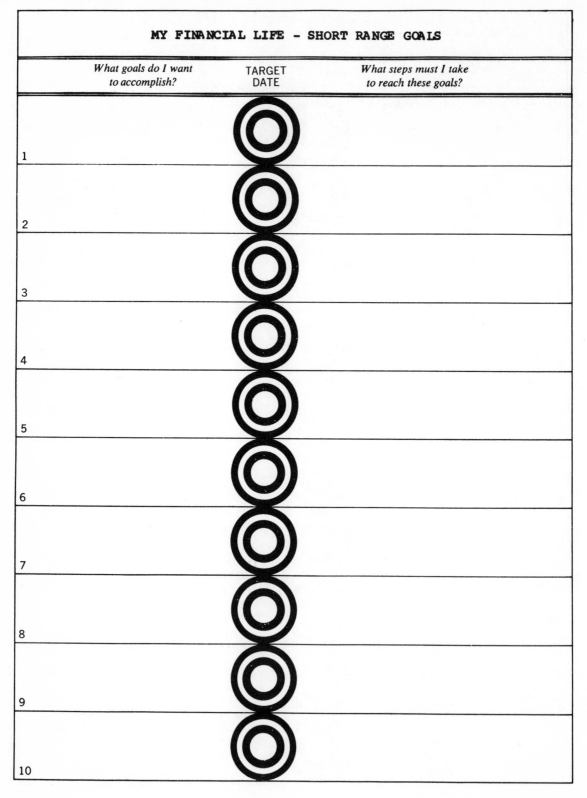

	What goals do I want to accomplish?	TARGET DATE	What steps must I take to reach these goals?
1			
2			
3			
4			
5			
6			
7			
8			
9			
10			

MY FINANCIAL LIFE - LONG RANGE GOALS

What goals do I want to accomplish?	TARGET DATE	*What steps must I take to reach these goals?*
1		
2		
3		
4		
5		
6		
7		
8		
9		
10		

77

MY PLAN

What do I really want to accomplish? _____
_____
_____
_____
_____
_____

What is the most effective and expedient way of reaching my goal? _____
_____
_____
_____
_____
_____

I have the following abilities, skills, and knowledge for achieving this goal: ____
_____
_____
_____
_____

Additional information, skills, and abilities needed: _____
_____
_____
_____
_____

Here are the places I will go, the people I will see, the sources I will use, to help me gain new knowledge, skills and abilities I need: _____
_____
_____
_____
_____
_____

The first step I will take this week: _____
_____

My next main steps will be as follows (Include deadlines): _____
_____
_____
_____
_____

My target date for reaching this goal: _____

78

MY SPECIFIC PLAN

What do I really want to accomplish?

TARGET DATE FOR COMPLETION

What is the most effective and expedient way of reaching my goal?

TARGET
DATE

My knowledge, skills, and abilities to help me achieve this goal:

Here is the exact first step I will take this week.

TARGET
DATE

Additional information, skills, and abilities needed:

My next main step:

TARGET
DATE

Places, people, sources I will use to gain new information.

My next main step:

TARGET
DATE

Your life is like a book. The title page is your name; the preface, your introduction to the world. The pages are a daily record of your efforts, trials, pleasures, discouragements. Day by day your thoughts and acts are being inscribed in your book of life. Hour by hour, the record is being made that must stand for all time. One day the word "finis" must be written. Let it then be said of your book that it is a record of noble purpose, generous service, and work well done.

—Grenville Kleiser

Section Three

PERSONAL

A brook—how like life. It too takes its beginning in mystery, and, like the little brook begins its meandering journey down the canyon that we call years—sometimes through sunny places, sometimes through shadowy, treacherous places, but ever going on, intent to reach some good.

—A. P. GOUTHEY

FOUNDATION STONES

In building a firm foundation for Success, here are a few stones to remember:

1. The wisdom of preparation.
2. The value of confidence.
3. The worth of honesty.
4. The privilege of working.
5. The discipline of struggle.
6. The magnetism of character.
7. The radiance of health.
8. The forcefulness of simplicity.
9. The winsomeness of courtesy.
10. The attractiveness of modesty.
11. The inspiration of cleanliness.
12. The satisfaction of serving.
13. The power of suggestion.
14. The buoyancy of enthusiasm.
15. The advantage of initiative.
16. The virtue of patience.
17. The rewards of co-operation.
18. The fruitfulness of perseverance.
19. The sportsmanship of losing.
20. The joy of winning.

—Rollo C. Hester

PERSONAL RESOURCES

Upon each individual rests the solemn obligation to make the most of himself. Most of us are capable of far more success and fulfillment in life than has actually come to us. Everyone is given twenty-four hours each day. You are anyone's equal when it comes to the amount of time daily given to everyone. How you use that time is what will make you unequal. Every man's greatest capital asset is his unexpired years of productive life.

The cornerstone of achievement and success is *DESIRE*. This is the starting point of a great career. It is the driving force of life, expansion and achievement. Hard work isn't enough to bring you success. It is intelligent well planned work that will bring you the rich rewards of life. We wonder why we don't get ahead faster, why we lost those friends, why we failed to get that order, why we went down in defeat in keen competition. We almost always look outside of ourselves to find the reason while we should look within for the answers.

Every single qualification for success is acquired through habit. Man is a bundle of habits, men form habits and habits form futures. If we do not deliberately form good habits, then we will unconsciously form bad ones. You are the kind of person you are because you have formed the habit of being that kind of person, and the only way you can change for the better, is through changing your habits.

It is an established fact that "success is a habit." Failure is also a habit. The important point is that man chooses his own pattern of thought. He makes his own blueprints of his future. He selects his own methods. Man makes the man. No one else does it for him. He does the job himself. Man creates his own success but he also creates his own failure. Success is not an accident, the key is to acquire the right habits.

Strong men are developed in the adversities and hardships of their lives. Hardships help a man to grow strong, virile, efficient. Strong muscles are produced in the gymnasium of necessity. Strong faith can only be produced amid darkness, discouragement, and seemingly hopeless situations. I don't believe there are any successful men who have not gone through the wringer.

The greatest desire of a man's heart is for happiness. There is no bank account that can balance a sweet, gracious personality; no material wealth can match a sunny heart, an ability to radiate helpfulness and sweetness.

Have you found yourself? Or is your life simply a vague daily grind without a definite goal, purposeless, monotonous, discouraged? Have you the ambition and will power to set about now to make your life what it should be—constructive, progressive, satisfying? All of the instruction there is, plus all of the wisdom and experience, means nothing unless you will use it.

PERSONAL LIFE

Each day is a little life; every waking and rising a little birth, every fresh morning a little youth, every going to rest and sleep a little death.

For the morning is the youth of the day, when everything is bright, fresh, and easy of attainment; we feel strong then, and all our faculties are completely at our disposal.

In making his way through life, a man will find it useful to be ready and able to do two things: to look ahead and to overlook; the one will protect him from loss and injury, the other from disputes and squabbles.

To overcome difficulties is to experience the full delight of existence, no matter where the obstacles are encountered; whether in the affairs of life, in commerce or business; or in mental effort—the spirit of inquiry that tries to master its subject. There is always something pleasurable in the struggle and the victory.

The world is in a very bad way. In savage countries they eat one another, in civilized countries they deceive one another; and that is what people call the way of the world.

No man is so formed that he can be left entirely to himself, to go his own ways; everyone needs to be guided by a preconceived plan, and to follow certain general rules.

Money is never spent to so much advantage as when you have been cheated out of it; for at one stroke you have purchased prudence.

In the great moments of life, when a man decides upon an important step, his action is directed not so much by any clear knowledge of the right thing to do, as by an inner impulse—you may almost call it an instinct or feel—proceeding from the deepest foundations of his being.

—Arthur Schopenhauer

A WELL BALANCED PERSONAL LIFE

Abraham Lincoln's formula for balanced living was simple: "Do not worry; eat three square meals a day; say your prayers; be courteous to your creditors; keep your digestion good; exercise; go slow and easy. Maybe there are other things that your special case requires to make you happy, but, my friend, these I reckon will give you a good lift."

In the modern business world it is very hard for us to keep our life simple, and balanced. In our over anxiety to make a success of our financial and business life we sometimes find ourselves neglecting our family, our health, our personal desires. But to be happy, to be truly successful over the long run of our lives we must fully develop every facet of our lives—not just a few.

It is the right balance to strive for in life, not too much, not too little. This applies to eating, drinking, sex, work, or any human appetite. Let moderation be your watchword. Moderation is the essence of all wisdom.

Always keep in mind that man is to be taken as a *WHOLE MAN* and that to function properly, efficiently and happily he should equally develop the three major areas of his life.

First, the physical life which concerns health, physical agility, exercise, nutrition, and the like. Our bodies house all of our abilities and ambitions, it is all that we have with which to meet nature and the elements. We must therefore keep fit in order to assure ourselves of the maximum use of our human potential.

Secondly, we have the mental portion of us which concerns our mental health, intellectual capacity, our thoughts, mental attitudes, and proper use of our mind power. Growth requires our constant personal effort.

Thirdly, our spiritual side which is the deepest desires of our soul expressing themselves through love, kindness, faith, ambition. All great men who contributed to their age and to society through government, business, art and the like had a fully developed spiritual nature—it was often the core of their success. For the spiritual values are what, in the last analysis, give us meaning and purpose for our lives.

In making your personal plans and goals take into consideration the proper balancing of these three elements in your life. One of the main differences between the successful man and the failure is the important aspect of "balance." Plan for time and activities which concern good health, mental growth, spiritual expression. Be a complete person fully capable of dealing with all that comes your way. Learn to live so as to enjoy each day to the uttermost.

Behind every successful man you will find a good woman. There is a woman at the beginning of all great things.

MY PERSONAL RECORD

My Name_____Social Security #_____

    Birthdate_____Birthplace_____

    _____Citizenship_____

    Blood Type_____ RH_____Height_____Weight_____

    Color of eyes_____Hair_____

    Heart trouble_____Epilepsy_____

    Diabetes_____Allergies_____

My Wife's Name_____(Maiden)_____

    Social Security #_____

    Birthdate_____Birthplace_____

    _____Citizenship_____

    Blood Type_____ RH_____Height_____Weight_____

    Color of eyes_____Hair_____

    Heart trouble_____Epilepsy_____

    Diabetes_____Allergies_____

My Father's Name_____Birthdate_____

    Address_____

    Birthplace_____

My Mother's Name_____Birthdate

    Address_____

    Birthplace_____

My Father-in-Law's Name_____

    Address_____

    Birthplace_____Birthdate_____

My Mother-in-Law's Name_____

    Address_____

    Birthplace_____Birthdate_____

This information will be helpful to you when filling out various
forms, as well as to remind you of your age before making investments, changing jobs, etc. Complete family records are in the
Family and Home Section pages 166-181.

EDUCATIONAL RECORD

Education is the harmonious development of all our faculties. It begins in the nursery, and goes on at school, but does not end there. It continues through life, whether we will or not. The only question is whether what we learn in life is wisely chosen or picked up haphazardly.

                                                    --John Lubbock

Attended From--To	Name of School	Location	Major & Degrees	Activities

RECORD OF SPECIAL TRAINING

(Such as night school, on job training, adult education, lectures, or special proficiencies you may have learned along the way.)

88

LIST OF MY ACCOMPLISHMENTS

List on this page specific accomplishments you have successfully
completed that have added to your personal qualities, experiences,
abilities. (Examples: schools, diplomas, degrees, clubs, community activities, hobbies, special talents, avocations, patents,
titles of offices held, civic duties; engineer, writer, singer,
inventor, world traveller, etc.)

Each accomplishment in life is meant only as a stepping stone
to the next more important accomplishment. No person ever has,
or ever will truly succeed without the application of this principle of constant achievement.

Associate With Great Men . . .

No man is great in and of himself; he must touch the lives of other great beings who will inspire him, lift him, and push him forward.

PROFESSIONAL ADVISORS

When you need advice, or information, go to the experts.
This is a cardinal principle. Everyone should know well
at least two or three older capable men to whom he can
go when he wants the teaching of experience and guidance.

MY ATTORNEY	MY INSURANCE AGENT
Name	Name
Firm	Firm
Address	Address
Telephone	Telephone

MY BANKER	MY ARCHITECT
Name	Name
Bank	Firm
Address	Address
Telephone	Telephone

MY ACCOUNTANT	MY MINISTER
Name	Name
Firm	Church
Address	Address
Telephone	Telephone

MY STOCK BROKER	MY DOCTOR
Name	Name
Firm	Group
Address	Address
Telephone	Telephone

MY TAX ADVISOR	MY DENTIST
Name	Name
Firm	Group
Address	Address
Telephone	Telephone

MY REAL ESTATE BROKER	OTHER:
Name	Name
Firm	Firm
Address	Address
Telephone	Telephone

PERSONAL ADVISORS
(In addition I consult the following persons)

Name	Name
Address	Address
Telephone	Telephone
Subject	Subject

Name	Name
Address	Address
Telephone	Telephone
Subject	Subject

MY SERVICE RECORD

Learn and practice the five army rules:

Preparing - Planning - Surprise

Adaptability - Fortitude.

Name_____Serial #_____M.O.S.#_____

Enlisted or inducted:_____Date_____Place_____Age_____

Branch of Service_____Grade_____

Training camps_____

Service Schools Attended_____

Division   Regiment   Dept/ship   Dates

Company

Transfered

Promotions and dates_____

Oversees Service: Dept._____Date_____Port_____
                  Return Date_____Port_____
                  Dept._____Date_____Port_____
                  Return Date_____Port_____

Battles, engagements, skirmishes, expeditions:_____

Commanding Officers_____

Citations_____

In service wounds, sickness,hospitalization_____

Important leaves or furloughs_____

Discharge/Separation:Place_____Grade_____Age_____

Reserve term_____Beg. Grade_____End Grade_____Dates_____

CLUBS AND ORGANIZATIONS

Groups to which I have belonged such as:
boy scouts, youth organizations, woodcraft,
YMCA, fraternities, societies, fraternal
orders, associations, professional organizations, country clubs, private clubs, civic
and community groups.

Date From-To	Name of Group	Address	Dues	Remarks

I WOULD

I WOULD have neither joy nor success by incurring a debt to others greater than I can pay. I would give value received for all I draw from the Bank of Life.

I WOULD have a few friends who know me for what I am and who love me in spite of what I am. In return for such friendship, I give my pledge to foster in myself what I ask of others.

I WOULD have some work to do which has such value that without it the day in which I live will be poorer, and richer if I succeed; and I want to do my work without taxing the purse, sympathy, or patience of others beyond the value that I give.

I WOULD cultivate such courage of mind and heart that I shall not be afraid to travel where there is no blazed trail, and I shall not hesitate to sacrifice when, by sacrificing, I can make contribution to others.

I WOULD experience such growth in grace as shall enable me to understand those who rejoice or weep or suffer. I would enter into their joy without covetousness and into their suffering with such sympathy as will give rise to courage and wings of hope.

I WOULD have a deeper appreciation of nature in all her moods and aspects, and a profounder respect for man as he seeks to labor together with God for the highest good of humanity.

I WOULD cultivate a sense of humor, for, without it, I have discovered life is likely to become so serious a business that it will be unlivable. Especially, would I learn to laugh at momentary defeat, smile at gray-cloaked discouragement, and dismiss dejection with the nonchalant carelessness of faith.

I WOULD learn to patiently endure little folk, with the full knowledge that time will soon release me from the annoyance of their littleness.

I WOULD have a little leisure in which to do—nothing. To keep the bow tightly strung all the time is, I have learned, to rob it of its spring and power. Too, I must have time to cultivate the fine art of meditation. God has His best chance at me when I am full of—hush.

Finally, *I WOULD* learn to wait for the best and have the wisdom to know it when it comes.

—A. P. Gouthey

BIOGRAPHICAL SKETCH

Tell your personal history, emphasize your important experiences, family background, education, employment, career, profession, and business positions; special activities - clubs, education, travel, sports; special interests - hobbies, talents, abilities; personality traits, character traits; your aims, ambitions, desires.

95

PERSONAL ANALYSIS

The questions on the following five pages are to help you analyze yourself - your personality traits, ambitions, goals. Your object-ive answer to these questions will bring insight into your own self and stimulate your thoughts about goals to set for improvement and growth.

What do you feel are your strongest personal assets or abilities?__
_____
_____

Can you honestly say that you have been making full use of these assets or abilities?_____
_____

Are you always planning, striving for the better things in life?___
_____
_____

What would success really mean to you, specifically, personally?___
_____
_____

Do you understand that success is personal and that it is achieving what you want to achieve?_____
_____

Do you associate with successful people who are experienced in the same line as your goals are?_____
_____

Do you influence and encourage your mind by "auto-suggestion", "positive thinking", or "affirmations"?_____
_____

Have you reached decisions promptly and definitely on all occasions?
_____
_____

Do you recognize and grasp an opportunity at once, or wait until someone else has taken advantage of it and used it?_____
_____

Have you been either "over-cautious" or "under-cautious"?_____
_____

Are your opinions and decisions based upon guesswork, or upon accuracy of analysis and thought?_____
_____
_____
_____

Have you permitted procrastination or fear to decrease your efficiency? If so, how can you overcome this?_____

_____

How much time do you devote to unprofitable effort which you might use to better advantage?_____

_____

Do you check your day's activities to see where you can cut off unnecessary things? Do you ask yourself "how important is this in helping me achieve the things I really want in life?"_____

_____

_____

How can you re-budget your time and change your habits to make better and more effective use of your time?_____

_____

Are you sharper in the morning? afternoon? evening? Do you do your most important work when you are at your sharpest peak?_____

_____

_____

Do you possess perseverance and grim determination to finish what you start out to accomplish?_____

_____

In what ways have you improved your personality in the last year?_

_____

_____

Do you have a self-improvement program continually in force?_____

_____

_____

Is your relationship with your associates at work pleasant or unpleasant? If unpleasant, is the fault partly, or wholly yours?___

_____

Do you try to improve yourself by taking special training? adult education courses?_____

What are the things that genuinely give you personal satisfaction? List the things you enjoy doing._____

_____

_____

_____

_____

Some men succeed because they cheerfully pay the price of success, and others, though they may claim ambition and a desire to succeed, are unwilling to pay the price.

PERSONAL GOALS AND AMBITIONS

What goal will I establish as my personal objective for this year?
_____
_____

If I already have such an objective, how far along am I toward
achieving it?_____
_____

What is my one personal purpose or objective in life? Give details.
_____
_____
_____
_____

What are some of my personal ambitions?_____
_____
_____

Am I developing my abilities?_____
_____

What can you do to make yourself worth more to your present employ
er, or in your present business?_____
_____
_____

Where would you like to be two years from now in your job, family
life, and personal improvement?_____
_____
_____
_____
_____

Where would you like to be ten years from now in your job, family
life, personal improvement, achievements, income rate?_____
_____
_____
_____
_____
_____

What factors do you need to bring into your life, new knowledge,
abilities, people, to accomplish your two and ten year goals?_____
_____
_____
_____
_____

Am I willing to endure the pain of struggle for the comforts and
rewards and the glory that go with achievement?_____
_____
_____
_____

PERSONAL QUESTIONNAIRE

What kind of person are you? What do you think of yourself as an individual? Make a complete written analysis. What are your strong points, your weak points?_____
_____
_____
_____
_____

How do you see yourself as a marriage partner? What does your wife or husband think of you?_____
_____
_____
_____

Is your home life happy and congenial?_____
_____

Do you have special family problems you would like solved? What are they and how would you suggest they be resolved?_____
_____
_____

Describe the image you hold of yourself as a parent. What kind of picture do you give to your children?_____
_____
_____

Describe your self-image as a friend. What is the picture you convey at meetings, social gatherings, and the like?_____
_____

Specifically, in what way would you like to change your self-image in terms of your family, your friends, and your contacts with others?_____
_____
_____

What personality characteristics would you like to change?_____
_____
_____
_____

List the self-improvements you are going to make_____
_____
_____
_____
_____
_____
_____

99

PERSONAL INTERESTS AND ACTIVITIES

We often limit our personal achievements and growth because we are not doing the right things. Answer the following questions about your general interests and activities. Then analyze the over-all picture. Are the things you are doing now helping you to build your character, and expand your horizons so that you will become worth more to yourself, your family, and your employer?

How do you spend most of your leisure time?_____
_____
_____

What magazines do you read regularly? Why? What do they do for you?
_____
_____

What newspapers do you read? How much time do you spend at it?____
_____

What TV programs do you see regularly? Why? Are they elevating, entertaining, just time consuming, or just habit?_____
_____
_____

What type of motion pictures do you choose? Why? How often do you attend?_____
_____

What type of music do you listen to?_____
What spectator sports do you like? How often do you attend? Why?_
_____

What sports do you participate in? How often?_____
_____

What old habits would you like to break and what new habits can you cultivate that will make you a more efficient and useful person?___
_____
_____
_____
_____

Are you wasting too much time?_____
_____

What new activities and interests would you like to have?_____
_____
_____

The great business of man lies in his ability to correct his mistakes and continually to make a new man of himself.

100

MY PERSONAL LIFE – SHORT RANGE GOALS

What goals do I want to accomplish?	TARGET DATE	What steps must I take to reach these goals?
1		
2		
3		
4		
5		
6		
7		
8		
9		
10		

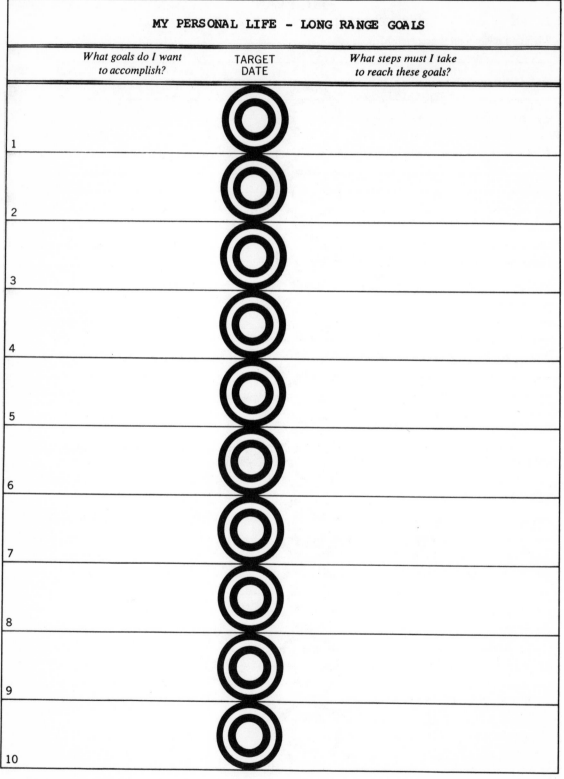

MY PERSONAL LIFE - LONG RANGE GOALS

	What goals do I want to accomplish?	TARGET DATE	What steps must I take to reach these goals?
1			
2			
3			
4			
5			
6			
7			
8			
9			
10			

MY PLAN

What do I really want to accomplish? _____
_____
_____
_____
_____
_____

What is the most effective and expedient way of reaching my goal?_____
_____
_____
_____
_____
_____

I have the following abilities, skills, and knowledge for achieving this goal:_____
_____
_____
_____
_____

Additional information, skills, and abilities needed:_____
_____
_____
_____
_____

Here are the places I will go, the people I will see, the sources I will use, to help me gain new knowledge, skills and abilities I need: _____
_____
_____
_____
_____
_____

The first step I will take this week:_____
_____

My next main steps will be as follows (Include deadlines):_____
_____
_____
_____
_____

My target date for reaching this goal: _____

MY SPECIFIC PLAN

What do I really want to accomplish?   TARGET DATE FOR COMPLETION

What is the most effective and expedient way of reaching my goal?

TARGET
DATE

My knowledge, skills, and abilities to help me achieve this goal:

Here is the exact first step
I will take this week.

TARGET
DATE

Additional information, skills, and abilities needed:

My next main step:

TARGET
DATE

Places, people, sources I will use to gain new information.

My next main step:

TARGET
DATE

WORTH QUOTING

The true teacher is life itself, and the world, is the only school room in which we can learn what we so evidently require.

—Manly P. Hall

Life is a leaf of paper white, whereon, each one of us may write his word or two, and then comes night; greatly begin! Tho thou hast time but for a line, be that sublime! Not failure, but low aim, is crime.

—James Russell Lowell

Be candid with yourself. Would you like to have a strong novelist like Dickens, or Hugo, or Balzac, describe you just as you are—acts, words, thoughts, motives—turning the light on so that the whole world would know the exact truth about you? What changes would you like to make in the picture? Are you the kind of man you would like to see the world made of? If not, why not? What improvements must you make in yourself in order to win your own approval and be the type of man you would be willing to see increase, and multiply, and occupy the earth?

—Councillor

Experience has taught me that financial success, job success, and happiness in human relations are in the main, the result of: (1) Physical well-being. (2) Constant effort to develop one's personal assets. (3) Setting up and working toward a series of life's goals. (4) Allowing time for meditation and spiritual regeneration.

—Roger Babson

It will take courage to cut away from the thousand and one hindrances that make life complex, but it can be done!

—Rhoda Lachar

Not infrequently do men of promise fail to achieve strong character for want of a great trial. When adversity does come—as it is sure to—they fall all to pieces for want of the fibre that only testing and drudgery can build into them.

—A. P. Gouthey

Decide what you want and write your goals. Then convert your goals into positive, present tense statements called affirmations. Affirm your goals each day until they become part of your sub-conscious mechanism. "As a man thinketh, so is he."

—*Executive Power*

Everybody wants to be somebody; nobody wants to grow.

—Goethe

Nothing is lost upon a man who is bent upon growth; nothing is wasted on one who is always preparing for his work and his life by keeping eyes, mind, and heart open to nature, men, books, experience. Such a man finds ministers to his education on all sides; everything cooperates with his passion for growth.

—H. Mabie

A BUSINESSMAN'S PHILOSOPHY

1. Do the *BEST* you can each day.

2. *THINK* and *PLAN* first, then *DO* secondly, then *ENJOY* the *FRUITS* of your labor.

3. Do not waste *TIME,* for time is the *RAW MATERIAL OF LIFE.*

4. Live *CONSTRUCTIVELY* and live *OPTIMISTICALLY.*

5. *LIVE* to *ENJOY* the money you make.

6. Abide by the *GOLDEN RULE*—Matthew 7:12.

7. Abide by the *SERMON ON THE MOUNT*—Matthew 5–6–7.

8. Nothing in life is *STATIC;* one must *LEARN* to make adjustments.

9. Never admit defeat. *LIVE CONFIDENTLY.*

10. Always look for the *GOOD* in the other fellow; no one is perfect.

11. Think *WELL* of yourself, as the world takes you at your own estimate.

12. Beware of *THIRST* for the wrong kind of pleasures; cut off wrong pleasures and replace them with the *REAL PLEASURES* of life.

13. *UNDERSTAND* the Law of *CAUSE* and *EFFECT.* I will suffer if I violate it. It becomes my greatest friend if I understand it.

14. Every *EXCESS* has its *EFFECT,* its *AFTERMATH,* its *HANGOVER. EVERYTHING* that exceeds the *BOUNDS OF MODERATION* has an *UNSTABLE FOUNDATION.*

15. *HAPPINESS* depends not on things around me, but on my *ATTITUDE.* Everything in my life will depend upon my *ATTITUDE.*

16. *YOU* serve *GOD* best by serving your fellow man.

—A. A. M.

106

WHAT IS MY PHILOSOPHY OF LIFE?

It is good for us to put in writing the conclusions we have drawn from our many life experiences. See if you can crystallize some of your values here. Much of our life is lived on the surface, and seldom, if ever, do we penetrate to the depths of our own existence. We become so involved, and so busy in our daily routine of getting and spending, that we forget the deepest questions of life.

Answering these questions will aid you in planning your future personal development. A personal philosophy and a practical religion will help a person navigate in the heavy seas that occasionally engulf one's life.

Spell out your philosophy of life. What do you believe?

What do you think about:

Life	Philosophy	Honesty
Money	Hope	Wealth
Health	Patience	Beauty
Happiness	Art	Joy
Love	Time	Conviction
God	Greatness	Fortitude
Nature	Marriage	Meditation
Music	Courage	Constructive Thinking
Prayer	Goodness	Peace of Mind
Morality	Manners	Rest
Society	Tact	Nutrition
Man	Habit	Exercise
Knowledge	Moderation	Humor
Truth	Ethics	Self-Discipline
Faith	Service	Judgment
Wisdom	Gratitude	Awareness
Planning	Education	Enthusiasm
Friendship	Sympathy	Optimism
Work	Integrity	Kindness
Death	Loyalty	Spiritual Fiber

What good is our present progress through technology and science if we fail to become better people? The fact is, that each of us is responsible for what we make of our own life. "Society" cannot play God and create people who are identical in ability. This development is an individual responsibility. This Manual will be a useful tool for each individual reader to forge his own success in whatever field his God-given talents allow.

MAKE SURE FIRST

Each passing day brings its peculiar burden and responsibility. *From this warfare,* to paraphrase Solomon, *there is no discharge.* Night and day one lives with the care and anxiety of it. On the other hand, each day brings its joy and compensation.

OCCUPATIONAL-
BUSINESS

A fundamental characteristic of a well-organized businessman is a plan for future growth. A man can promote himself to almost any position he desires by the simple process of getting himself ready to fill the job. Be prepared for the next position above.

One of the hardest things in the world to discover is one's own aptitude. Ask yourself the following questions: What is my mission in life? What is my work? What are my talents? What faculties do I possess? What am I best fitted for?

—Owen D. Young

SEEKING A JOB

If you are seeking work tell the employer what you can do for him. Unless you have some reasonable proof that your services are worth more than you are getting, say nothing about more pay. The secret of success in life is for a man to be ready for his opportunity when it comes.

The best ways to find a job are through: Information from friends . . . newspaper advertisements . . . employment agencies . . . resume mail campaigns . . . and direct contact with firms.

Whatever method you use, be prepared to answer these questions: How old are you? Why are you thinking of leaving your present job? What is your greatest asset as an employee? What is your greatest liability? How much money do you want? How long do you expect to stay with us? Why do you want to work for us?

You should expect to stand an investigation of your educational background, your military record, your previous positions, and your general reputation.

These characteristics are sure to be evaluated: Your mental capacity . . . your physical condition . . . your moral standards . . . your personality . . . your personal appearance.

Your opportunity for obtaining employment depends upon the economy of a particular job market, personal contacts, and being at the right place at the right time.

When looking for a better position while still holding a job, it is important—(1) to make inquiries more discreetly; (2) to keep your present work up to a high standard, and (3) to leave gracefully and pleasantly when you do obtain your new position. A person who is employed has an advantage over an unemployed job seeker in that he not only can take a longer period of time to search and therefore be more particular in what he takes; but he can generally command a better salary than the man who isn't making any money at all.

SEEKING A PROMOTION

If you are seeking a promotion, more responsibility, or higher pay from your employer there are certain conditions you must meet before you can expect the company to re-evaluate your worth. A company needs quality in its employees or it cannot stay in business. If you are better than the average you will be paid more than the average.

You must prove, however, that you are better than the average. How do you attain this? Not by a temporary spurt of enthusiasm which dies off as soon as you are recognized, but by a consistent program of personal growth, increased productivity, and increased quality of out-put. To earn more you must be worth more.

Any man's worth to any business is his ability to deliver.

—Roy L. Smith

TEN COMMANDMENTS OF SUCCESS

Work hard.   Hard work is the best investment a man can make.

Study hard.   Knowledge enables a man to work more intelligently and effectively.

Have initiative.   Ruts often deepen into graves.

Love your work.   Then you will find pleasure in mastering it.

Be exact.   Slipshod methods bring slipshod results.

Have the spirit of conquest. Thus you can successfully battle and overcome difficulties.

Cultivate personality.   Personality is to a man what perfume is to the flower.

Help and share with others.   The real test of business greatness lies in giving opportunity to others.

Be democratic.   Unless you feel right towards your fellow man you can never be a successful leader of men.

In all things do your best.   The man who has done less than his best has done nothing.

—Charles M. Schwab

EMPLOYMENT RECORD

Life requires that we work (work being simply the opposite of rusting away), and nature requires that we work at something we were designed to do. Such activity is exhilerating, interesting. It begets energy, health, and happiness. It defeats tensions.

--Hal Falvey

Dates From- To	Employer	Address	Position	Salary	Immediate Superior	Reason For Leaving

RESUME WORKSHEET
Basic Information To Help You Write Your Resume

PERSONAL: Birthdate_____Birthplace_____Soc.Sec.#_____
Citizenship_____Height____Weight____Health_____
Handicaps_____Marital Status_____Dependents_____
Travel/Amount_____Relocate/Where_____

MILITARY: Branch_____Serial #_____From/To_____
Type Discharge_____Rank_____Duties_____

EDUCATION: High School_____Location_____
From_____To_____Credits_____Major_____
College_____Location_____
From_____To_____Credits_____Major_____
Years Completed_____Degree Received_____
Honors and scholarships granted_____

Organization memberships_____

Trade, vocational or business schools_____

Dates attended_____Course of Study_____
Degree Received_____Date Received_____
Special courses taken_____

SPECIAL SKILLS: (Type, ability level) _____

Machines and Equipment Used_____

Licenses or Certificates Held_____

Publications, articles, papers written_____

HONORS AWARDS: Type, when, where and amount_____

LANGUAGES: Language_____Read___Speak_____Write_____
Language_____Read___Speak_____Write_____
Can you translate?_____

REFERENCES: Name_____Address_____
Business_____Time Known_____
Name_____Address_____
Business_____Time Known_____
Name_____Address_____
Business_____Time Known_____

EXPERIENCE: (Work with employment record Page 113. Describe the duties you performed, and your accomplishments for your last five employers).

114

HOW TO COMPILE A RESUME

No matter what kind of employment you are seeking, you are in competition. The resume is your best tool for presenting to your prospective employer your qualifications. The purpose of the resume is to pinpoint your main sales message to secure a personal interview. It also focuses the interviewer's attention on your best qualifications. It is something tangible to leave behind so the interviewer remembers who you are and what you can do.

Your resume is the first impression you give—it should be neat, short (one page is best, two are acceptable). Include the most important data that shows your qualifications for the job you are seeking. It should be conservative, and well done.

Keep your resume factual—what you have *done* is what counts, not what you think of yourself. Information that is not vital to the job you are applying for can be left out. Decide what job you want and make that job the title of your resume. For instance —"Sales Manager," "Cost Accountant."

Information to Include: At the top of the page give your name, address, and telephone number where you can be reached during working hours. Then in the first paragraph give a wrap-up summary of your experience designed to catch the eye of a busy executive.

Next give your employment record in reverse chronological order, or by the function you performed. Include your job title, name of the firm, period of employment (month and years). Your actual duties and responsibilities. It is your highest level experience in each job that means the most. It is not necessary to mention lower level jobs unless they will show how fast you were promoted. Stress what you yourself did.

Next list your special accomplishments or commendations. What did you accomplish for the companies you worked for—saved money, made money, adopted a new system, re-organized a department.

Then give your educational background. Your highest schooling is listed first. If you are a college graduate you may skip your secondary schooling. If business experience or work experience is lacking, then use more details on educational background. Mention campus activities only if they help establish your qualifications for the job you are seeking.

Other qualifications to list: have you travelled, do you speak, read or write any foreign language, have you published articles in your field, do you belong to professional or business associations? List those qualifications that have direct bearing on the job you are seeking. Then give your personal data; age and marital status; a good photograph. You may mention your military service. Personal references and salary figures are for the personal interview and need not be included in the resume.

WHERE THE MONEY IS

What are the top paying occupations in the country? The Labor Department has estimated annual earnings of male workers on the basis of 1965 census interviews. Here are the top 50 occupations according to their earnings. These are median figures . . . half the individuals in each occupation earn more than the figure shown and half earn less:

Physicians	$14,561
Managers, self-employed, banking and other finance	12,757
Dentists	11,858
Professors, instructors, medical sciences	11,666
Lawyers, judges	10,587
Airplane pilots, navigators	10,274
Osteopaths	10,128
College presidents, deans	9,704
Managers, self-employed, insurance, real estate	9,410
Managers, salaried, manufacturing	9,090
Physicists	9,043
Aeronautical engineers	9,018
Veterinarians	8,882
Chemical engineers	8,810
Sales engineers	8,694
Architects	8,651
Economists	8,649
Electrical engineers	8,553
Metallurgical engineers	8,534
Geologists, geophysicists	8,409
Optometrists	8,404
Mining engineers	8,359
Mechanical engineers	8,355
Managers, salaried, business services	8,340
Managers, salaried, insurance, real estate	8,231
Engineers, technical	8,062
Professors, instructors, agricultural sciences	7,918

Managers, salaried, communications, utilities	7,916
Professors, instructors, engineering	7,841
Public relations	7,826
Professors, psychology	7,811
Mathematicians	7,780
Managers, self-employed, manufacturing	7,736
Psychologists	7,726
Industrial engineers	7,673
Managers, salaried, construction	7,632
Civil engineers	7,606
Locomotive engineers	7,586
Professors, social sciences	7,510
Personnel, labor relations	7,490
Managers, self-employed, wholesale trade	7,465
Professors, economics	7,447
Managers, salaried, banking and finance	7,439
Professors, biological sciences	7,410
Managers, self-employed, business services	7,399
Professors, instructors, physics	7,373
Managers, salaried, transportation	7,351
Natural scientists	7,351
Professors, instructors, chemistry	7,340
Managers, salaried, wholesale trade	7,339

EMPLOYEE SUGGESTION PLAN

Zest for living is personified by a person who not only does his best, but is always learning a little more than he needs to know, doing a little more than the job calls for, or having a faith beyond its own needs so he can share it with others. Such a person usually receives rewards he deserves plus a little more.

Here are the ABC's of suggesting improvements:—

A—Ask questions: Who, what, where, when, why, how.
B—Be sure you are doing the job in the best way.
C—Consider every angle of your job. There's always a better way.
D—Develop a sense of curiosity. Why do we do a job this way?
E—Eliminate all unnecessary parts of your job, such as duplication, wasted time or materials.

F—First be sure you know all about your job, then suggest a better way.
G—Gain extra recognition through your ideas.
H—Hard work can often be lightened by using your ideas.
I—Ideas mean money and easier work for everybody.
J—Just be alert. Ideas are all around you. Learn to recognize them.

K—Keep submitting suggestions. Good ones always pay.
L—Let your supervisor help you work out details. He'll be glad to help with your suggestion.
M—Make your past experience pay off by proposing better ways to do a job.
N—Never overlook any portion of your work. Why do you perform each step? Is it necessary? Can it be improved?
O—Other fellows' complaints may be things that need improving. Propose a remedy.

P—Prepare suggestions completely—giving location, department or number, job title, etc. Ideas can be evaluated quicker and better if the evaluating department knows what you mean.
Q—Quit envying the fellow who gets the reward. Turn in your own ideas regularly and you'll get them too.
R—Remember to write down your ideas so you won't forget them.
S—Study all parts of your work and suggest a better way to do it.
T—Turn in at least one suggestion each week.

U—Use all available help. Your past experience, your reading and thinking will all help.
V—Very often a very simple idea saves a large amount of money or time. Turn in all your ideas.
W—Watch every move you make and look for an easier way to do your job.
X—Xtra recognition is waiting for your good ideas.
Y—You can add to your security by submitting valuable ideas regularly.
Z—Zoom your earnings

BUSINESS SUCCESS FORMULA

Carefully examine every detail of the business.

Be prompt.

Take time to consider and then decide quickly.

Dare to go forward.

Maintain your integrity as a sacred thing.

Never tell business lies.

Make no useless acquaintances.

Never try to appear something more than you are.

Pay your debts promptly.

Learn how to risk your money at the right time.

Shun strong liquor.

Employ your time well.

Do not reckon on chance.

Be polite to everyone.

Never be discouraged.

Work hard and you will succeed.

> —Written more than 100
> years ago by Baron von
> Rothschild.

BUSINESS

It is the close observation of little things which is the secret of success in business, in art, in science, and in every pursuit in life. Human knowledge is but an accumulation of small facts, made by successive generations of men—the little bits of knowledge and experience carefully treasured up and growing at length into a mighty pyramid.

—Samuel Smiles

Business is always a struggle. There are always obstacles and competitors. There is never an open road, except the wide road that leads to failure. Every great success has always been achieved by fight. Every winner has scars. The men who succeed are the efficient few. They are the few who have the ambition and will-power to develop themselves.

—Herbert N. Casson

BUSINESS KNOWLEDGE

A business succeeds or fails on the profit or losses it makes, and on that basis alone.

All progress calls for greater thought, action, and personal sacrifice. Results can only equal the investment. Triumph is the ripe fruit of sacrificial investment. Let us all be sure we do our best.

The first "industrial revolution" was from muscle power to machine power. The second industrial revolution now going on, is from electro-mechanical power to brain power. Automation—servomechanisms—advancing technology—have all played a dominant role in the genesis of the second industrial revolution. And this revolution, like the first, has brought about a great need for highly skilled employees.

Today, the development of your employees is vitally necessary. Investing in the people who are part of the bloodstream of your company is one of the best investments for your company.

The most important ingredient in the formula for success is good people. Without good people in all areas of operations—engineering, production, merchandising, administration, service, and management—the most modern, expensive and efficient buildings and machinery cannot turn out a quality product at a competitive price. Companies are people and when they end up with incompetent people they fail.

Employees of twenty-four large companies were asked to rank the ten morale factors in their order of importance. Here is their importance rating:

1. Full appreciation of work done.
2. Feeling "in" on things.
3. Good wages.
4. Sympathetic help on personal problems.
5. Job security.
6. Interesting work.
7. Promotion, growth, in company.
8. Personal loyalty to workers.
9. Good working conditions.
10. Tactful disciplining.

The ultimate boss that we all have is the customer. Regardless of what anyone may tell you about job security, unless your business can produce a quality product or service, sell it for a competitive price and still make enough profit to pay its shareholders a reasonable return and keep its plants and machinery in good shape, you have no job security. The buyer is going to spend his money where he is getting the best product or service for the least cost.

But what is good judgment but a product of your mental operations? And if these operations are logical, your judgment will be sound. If illogical, your judgments will be faulty. All kinds of haywire decisions can be arrived at, of course, from perfectly sound facts. So that I should say the statement commonly mouthed "A man's judgment is no better than his facts," should be changed to "a man's judgment is no better than his logical analysis of the facts."

—William J. Reilly

BUSINESS EXPERIENCE

Your present position_____
Company Name_____
Company Address_____Telephone_____
_____
Duties in your position_____
_____
_____
_____

Are you familiar with your company policies?_____
_____
How many people do you supervise?_____
_____

How do you look in the eyes of your boss? efficient, alert, trusting, dependable?_____

Do you like to assume responsibility?_____
_____

How are your relations with company personnel?_____
_____

What is the next advanced position you desire?_____
_____

What preparation is necessary to prepare you for it?_____
_____

Are you ready? For the opportunities always come when not expected.
_____

Do you have full knowledge of your company's products or services?
_____

Is there some innovation, new product, new management system you
can present to your company that will speed your advancement?_____
_____
_____
_____

Analyze the products and purposes of your company. What can you
do for them that will help them make more money, produce better
goods, work more efficiently?_____
_____
_____
_____
_____

Leadership is earned, not proclaimed.

STUDY IN FUTILITY

The remains of two warring bucks that were found in Texas. This drawing dramatically captures the battle of survival. Business likewise is the survival of the fittest.

124

COMPETITION

Competition comes in place of monopoly; and intelligence and industry ask only for fair play and an open field.

—Daniel Webster

The salesman, perhaps more than any other businessman, feels the pinch of competition. This competition is particularly strong in every field today. Of course, we really wouldn't want things to be any other way—for competition is the foundation which supports our free enterprise economy.

Yet salesmen often complain that "competition is too tough" or that they can't keep up with the big companies. They can't seem to find a solution. There is, however, an answer to stiff competition, and that is quality and service. A man who is selling a truly superior product or service will seldom have to fear being forced out by his competitors.

Competition is part of the game. Don't become personally hostile. Be able to accept hostility from others. The more successful the executive, the more he can dish out hostility and accept it, gracefully. You can let the competing executive know in no uncertain terms that you don't like his tactics, but do it with a minimum of hostility.

Our competitors are often our greatest benefactors. He that wrestles with us strengthens our muscles and sharpens our skill.

ETHICS

Ethics means right human conduct. The assumption is that we should be concerned not only with our own welfare but also with that of others.

Don't knock your employers. Don't knock the policy of your company. Don't knock your business associates. Don't knock anything or anybody in the business. Be loyal . . . boost! If you cannot boost the business you are in, get out of it.

Ethics is a silver thread in the fabric of our daily business life. It is always visible to the perceptive eye. It takes on a luminous glow when we perceive that ethical practices are part of the spiritual fiber of the man in management. If we were half as concerned about our own ethics as we are about the other fellow's, there would be no serious problem. Conscience dictates that virtue is an end in itself, not a pragmatic means to a material end. The compensation comes with satisfaction in doing "unto others as you would have them do unto you." Doing it without public incentive is good business ethics in both policy and principle.

The severest test of a businessman's acumen and ability sometimes lies in the speed and manner with which he recognizes and grasps the opportunities presented by the vagaries of Fate.

—J. Paul Getty

BUSINESS ADVICE

If I were to venture a forecast, I would say that business will be good this year for those who make it good.

—Clarence Goshorn

Business without profit is not business any more than a pickle is candy.

—Charles Abbott

Success or failure in business is caused more by mental attitude even than by mental capacities.

—Walter Dill Scott

Successful men usually snatch success from seeming failure. If they know there is such a word as failure they will not admit it. They may be whipped, but they are not aware of it. That is why they succeed.

—A. P. Gouthey

"Buy low—sell high" is an old businessman's maxim. This is probably the oldest trade principle in the world.

It is not the size that counts in business. Some companies with $500,000 capital net more profits than other companies with five million. Size is a handicap, unless efficiency goes with it.

—Herbert Casson

You are not here, gentlemen, to agree with me, but to express your own views. If you do that, I can compare them with mine and decide which is the better.

—Daryl Zanuch

Business is a battlefield, and the men who win are those armed with knowledge, new ideas, and superior methods.

Keep your organization flexible. Don't permit it to become muscle bound with rules and precedents.

Contrary to accepted thought; the good manager manages quite as much with his heart as with his head.

—Crawford H. Greenwalt

The right to become more efficient and grow is a basic concept of business. It's fundamental free enterprise.

—Charles Sommer

The most successful business man is the man who holds on to the old just as long as it is good and grabs the new just as soon as it is better.

—Robert P. Vanderpoel

Cultivate clear perception and good judgment. These are essential to financial success. Surround yourself with able associates and wide awake, capable employees. The man who has capital can usually find men without capital but who possess various forms of skill and knowledge, and an alliance of such forces is often productive of great benefit to both classes of men.

—Grenville Kleiser

THIS IS BUSINESS

. . . Business is getting up at six to meet a customer at eight who doesn't show up until ten.

. . . Business is pleading with your customer to be patient while you exercise the privilege of being impatient with your subordinates.

. . . Business is scheming ways by which you can help your customers to make an extra dollar in the hope that they will let you keep ten cents for yourself.

. . . Business is driving all day to see a man who is "in conference" when you get there.

. . . Business is reaching for the restaurant check and getting stuck with it nine times out of ten.

. . . Business is getting indigestion and liver trouble from entertaining the trade.

. . . Business is borrowing money to pay the tax collector.

. . . Business is pretending that you are prosperous when you haven't made a cent for two years.

. . . Business is showing a prospect how a job should be done and then having him give it to a competitor.

. . . Business is feeling happy about landing a big job on which you will probably lose your shirt.

. . . Business is erecting barriers against salesmen who want to see you and advising your own salesmen how to get through the barriers erected against them.

. . . Business is fun—if you like it!

—William Feather

BUSINESS CLUBS AND INDUSTRY GROUPS

List here your business clubs, trade associations, industry groups, to which you belong such as: Lions, Rotary, Kiwanis, Optimists, Elks, Toastmasters, American Legion, professional associations, trade associations. (Also see form pg. 93).

Date Joined	Name of Group	Address	Meetings	Dues	Remarks

PAST MEMBERSHIPS

Dates From-To	Name of Group	Offices Held	Remarks

Thousands of engineers can design bridges, calculate strains and stresses, and draw up specifications for machines, but the great engineer or administrator is the man who can tell whether the bridge or the machine should be built at all, where it should be built and when.

—E. G. Grace

EXECUTIVE SELF-RATING CHART

	Yes	No	Some-times
When credit is due others, I see that they get it.	___	___	___
I welcome new ideas and try to use them.	___	___	___
I look for ways to cut costs, increase profits.	___	___	___
I get a real kick out of the amount of work I do.	___	___	___
Overtime never bothers me; I expect it.	___	___	___
I read every trade magazine in my field.	___	___	___
I'd rather give others the benefit of the doubt than argue.	___	___	___
Some people I can't stand; but I try to be diplomatic.	___	___	___
I help others whether they reciprocate or not.	___	___	___
My people are given as much responsibility as they'll take.	___	___	___
When a job becomes routine, I assign it to others.	___	___	___
I look for new ways to expand my department's work.	___	___	___
If I make a wrong decision, I'll take the rap.	___	___	___
I'd rather make a faulty decision than waver.	___	___	___
I dislike criticism, but I can "take it".	___	___	___
Criticism has helped me improve in at least four ways.	___	___	___
I can listen to others without interrupting.	___	___	___
When others are talking, I concentrate on what they're saying.	___	___	___
When I feel discouraged, I try to redouble my efforts.	___	___	___
I consider loyalty and ethical conduct basic to long-run success.	___	___	___

OCCUPATIONAL - BUSINESS QUESTIONNAIRE

What do you think of yourself in your job? profession? business?
Are you outstanding, the very best, good, average, just getting
along?_____
_____
_____

Is your work, trade, vocation, one you are happy in and with?_____
_____
_____

Are you conscientious about the job you do? Do you do the best you
can each day?_____
_____

Do you learn and profit from your mistakes and recognize them as
opportunities?_____
_____

Do you try to make the work enjoyable for those around you?_____
_____

Are you continually looking for ways to improve the quality of your
work, the time it takes, the ease in doing it?_____
_____
_____

Do you recognize the level of your own abilities and talents and
try to cooperate and be useful to those who have greater abilities
that would take you along with them?_____
_____
_____

Do you see yourself as a great executive, partner, owner?_____
_____

Do you have the rare ability to recognize ability in others?_____
_____

What new skills do you need to earn advancement in your work?_____
_____
_____
_____

How can you make more money for your company?_____
_____
_____
_____
_____
_____

The road to the top is steep, it is not cheap.

132

SUGGESTED GOALS AND OBJECTIVES
For Your Occupational—Business Life

Study and work for the position above.

Develop self-discipline and enthusiasm for hard work.

Take self-improvement courses to increase my value.

Plan daily work, do things in order of their importance.

Increase my sales.

Help the company earn a good profit.

Develop cost-cutting methods for the company.

Be of greater service to my customers.

Be more cooperative and cheerful.

Learn the entire business and industry.

Make myself worth more so I can earn more.

An executive's job is getting things done through other people. The higher up the executive ladder you go the more heavily the problems listed below will weigh upon you:

1. Achieving the company's overall objectives.
2. Planning, and setting policies and objectives.
3. Making decisions, thinking, analyzing.
4. Coordinating functions and people.
5. Organizing and developing subordinates, advising other executives and managers.
6. Handling subordinates, controlling operations.
7. Improving own capacities, leading, setting an example.
8. Delegating, giving orders, working through others.
9. Exercising business judgement, performing a speciality.
10. Dealing with the public.
11. Improving the company's business in every way.

PROBLEM SOLVING

The most important thing is to *state the problem*. This is not as simple as it seems. To state the problem you must include a description of the situation you want when you get through. You must think through to the result and state the result you want. This often is the statement of the problem.

Problem solving formula: 1. Set down the problem in order to study and solve it. 2. Collect all the facts. 3. Study the facts, think about them. 4. Get possible solutions from trial and error. 5. Select the best possible solution from these.

Anyone who takes the time to look at the total situation has a far better chance of defining the real problem and considering all possible solutions. A good problem statement often includes (a) what is known, (b) what is unknown, (c) what is sought.

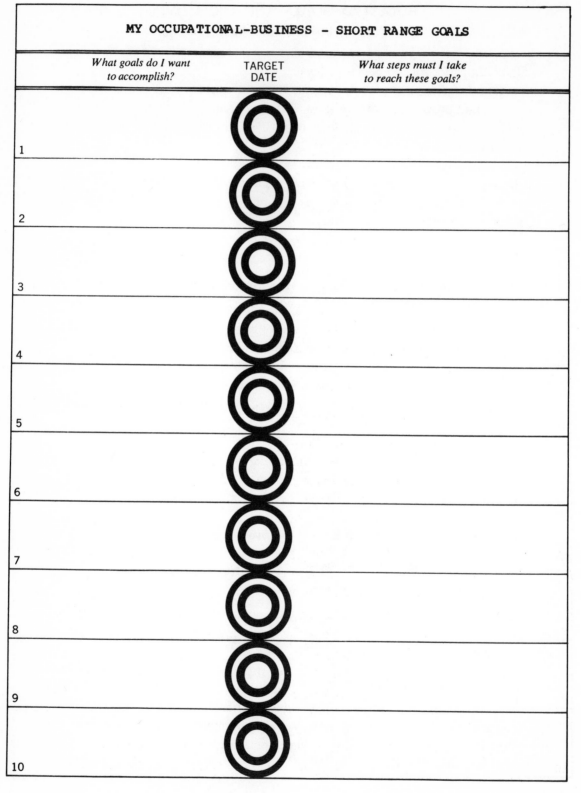

MY OCCUPATIONAL-BUSINESS - SHORT RANGE GOALS

What goals do I want to accomplish?	TARGET DATE	*What steps must I take to reach these goals?*
1		
2		
3		
4		
5		
6		
7		
8		
9		
10		

MY OCCUPATIONAL-BUSINESS - LONG RANGE GOALS

	What goals do I want to accomplish?	TARGET DATE	*What steps must I take to reach these goals?*
1			
2			
3			
4			
5			
6			
7			
8			
9			
10			

MY PLAN

What do I really want to accomplish? _____
_____
_____
_____
_____
_____

What is the most effective and expedient way of reaching my goal?_____
_____
_____
_____
_____
_____

I have the following abilities, skills, and knowledge for achieving this goal:_____
_____
_____
_____
_____

Additional information, skills, and abilities needed:_____
_____
_____
_____
_____

Here are the places I will go, the people I will see, the sources I will use, to help me gain new knowledge, skills and abilities I need: _____
_____
_____
_____
_____
_____

The first step I will take this week:_____
_____

My next main steps will be as follows (Include deadlines):_____
_____
_____
_____
_____

My target date for reaching this goal: _____

MY SPECIFIC PLAN

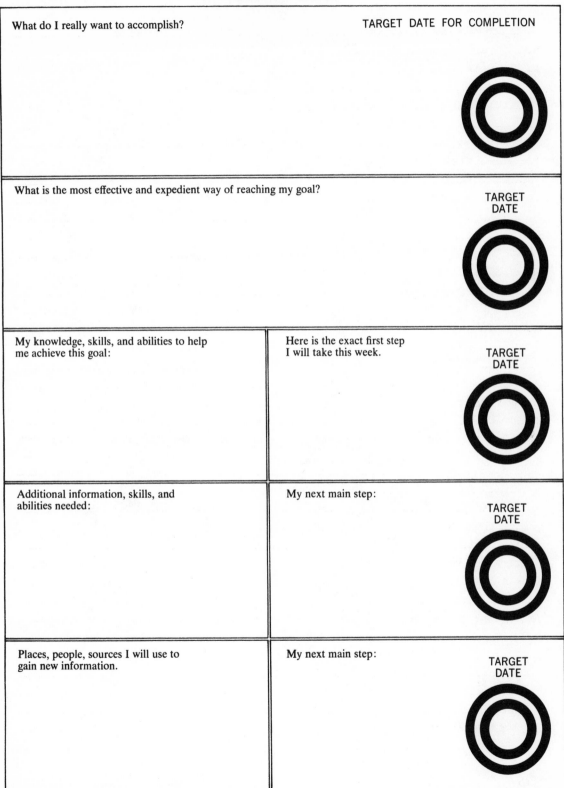

What do I really want to accomplish?

TARGET DATE FOR COMPLETION

What is the most effective and expedient way of reaching my goal?

TARGET
DATE

My knowledge, skills, and abilities to help me achieve this goal:

Here is the exact first step
I will take this week.

TARGET
DATE

Additional information, skills, and abilities needed:

My next main step:

TARGET
DATE

Places, people, sources I will use to gain new information.

My next main step:

TARGET
DATE

Section Five

HEALTH

Have regular checkups.

Work off tensions.

Make time for fun.

Walk for exercise.

138   Eat a balanced diet.

Sleep to restore nervous energy.

A man's best ally in his quest for success is physical health. Without it he can't stand the pace. As health depends on sleep, the man who means to succeed must determine to order his life so that he sleeps well and rests fully. His first step is to lead a wholesome life throughout the day. Keep meals simple. Chew all food thoroughly. Exercise all muscles daily. Be an optimist. Control anger, fear, and worry. Play moderately. Be temperate in every thing. Laugh often.

—GRENVILLE KLEISER

GUIDELINES FOR HEALTH

My biggest asset is the unexpired years that I have left.

Radiant, buoyant good health is life's choicest and most precious gift. It behooves us, then, to guard it well, using the laws of nature for its maintenance.

Given a perfect or near perfect body and body mechanism at birth, we can and must keep it in good condition by obeying the tenets of good health commandments. These include the basics for each person's individual need and set forth such factors as good and adequate nutrition, bodily exercise, mental activity, cleanliness, relaxation and sleep. These are the essentials for the enjoyment of good health.

Improper eating and physical idleness go together and thus men suffer from avoidable diseases which inflict upon them years of unnecessary ill health and suffering, followed by untimely death. Man is nourished not by the food he eats but only in proportion to what he is able to digest and assimilate.

Many doctors are coming to the conclusion that the primary cause of disease is not germs. Their belief is that disease is caused by toxemia (blood poisoning) which results in cellular impairment and breakdown, which disables the defense members of the body. This allows a way for the multiplication and onslaught of germs because of a disturbed function.

The word *toxemia* carries its own meaning, namely . . . *toxin* (blood poisoning) in the blood. Blood poisoning is caused by an above normal supply of broken down body cells, and is the primary cause of disease. Toxemia is self-poisoning by our improper habits, improper food, our excesses, and improper care of our body. This accounts for man's discomforts, sickness and death before full maturity. Sickness is most of our own building and unnecessary except to those who have no self-control.

139

People need to be taught self-control; to understand their self-limitations, and to exercise moderation in all things. The needs of each individual are made known to him by his hunger, or moderate desire. Those who abuse their privileges—their limitations—will be abused by appetite, uncontrollable desire, discomfort and so-called diseases. Every excess has its effect, its aftermath, its hangover.

Hippocrates, the father of medicine, taught men how to help mother nature in her work. He knew, too, that the laws of nature cannot be broken and that those laws do not change. His remedy is that disease can be cured through the proper use of the body and proper use of correct food. He stated, "Thy food shall be thy remedy," meaning foods that contain the natural chemicals which nature has provided. Nature does the real healing utilizing the natural defenses of the body.

CONTROL YOUR WEIGHT

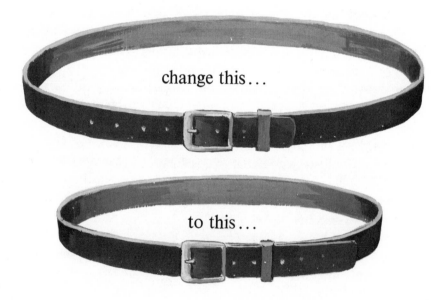

change this...

to this...

The way to reduce is to cut down on eating, not cut it out.
The ideal diet is expressed in three words—"No more please."
It's *YOU,* not the diet that's responsible.

140

YOU CAN BE WELL

Air and sun are foods, cleansers and tonics. We should endeavor to get as much fresh air and sunshine as possible, but we do not get the maximum benefit by exposing ourselves to air and sunlight in a state of inactivity.

How many mental giants have broken down from mental overwork solely because they lacked physical stamina. Overstress and strain, whether physical or emotional, can precipitate trouble.

One of the best antidotes for mental stress and emotional fatigue is physical fatigue from exercise. Much of the tranquilizing going on in this country today would be unnecessary if people could get physically tired and again sleep as they did in childhood, after a strenuous game.

Walking is more than excellent physical exercise. Walking fills the lungs with clean fresh air, purifying the blood and stimulating the mental faculties. Swimming is one of the finest exercises, golf is also excellent. If a person is not in good health he can retrain himself at any age . . . slowly, gradually getting back into condition. It is a matter of conditioning.

The biggest business any person can invest in which will bring the greatest profit is their health. Is a man actually successful if he reaches the top of his profession but is not able to live long enough to enjoy it? The answer is no. Let your motto be—live to enjoy the money you make.

So make the most of the state of health you possess. "Eat, drink and be merry" is good advice if followed in moderation. Substitute activity is relaxing, be it physical or mental exertion.

Simple rules which, if thoroughly learned and earnestly followed, will surely result in a better physical and mental condition. We see men managing their business with wisdom, while they manage their own bodies in folly. There are four habits that we must cultivate if we would be well. They are the habits of right thinking, right breathing, right eating, and right exercising.

The more man follows nature and is obedient to her laws, the longer he will live; the further he deviates from these, the shorter will be his existence. Health is nature's reward for getting into harmony with her laws. Without health, life is not life; it is only a state of languor and suffering. For life is not merely to be alive, but to be well. The building of a perfect body, crowned by a perfect brain, is the grandest hope of our civilization. A sound body lies at the foundation of all that goes toward making life a success.

YOUR HEALTH RECORD

Date	Illness/Surgery	Doctor/Hospital	Comments

HEALTH INSURANCE

Company_____
Policy #_____
Benefits_____

Company_____
Policy #_____
Benefits_____

VACCINATIONS

Tetanus_____
Small Pox_____
Typhoid_____
Polio _____
Other _____
_____
_____

My Blood Type_____RH Factor_____

Ailments I have_____
_____
_____

Medicines or antibiotics to which I am allergic or sensative_____
_____
_____

Other pertinent information_____
_____
_____

142

PRIMARY REQUIREMENTS OF HEALTH

A formula for good health is: eat nutritious food—control your weight—exercise a little every day—get enough sleep every night—keep calm and avoid emotional disturbances—think wholesome and constructive thoughts.

Correct eating is up to you. When you violate nature's laws and get sick you must correct your diet and take all the necessary steps to regain your health. Human nature does not like discipline, but the only way to return to health is to exercise discipline and restraint over your carelessness and excesses of the past.

Disease is mostly *self-created*. To be well, it is often only necessary to stop doing the things that are causing you to be sick. The only exception to this is where one has waited too long and nature has been so outraged and degeneration proceeded so far, that there is no turning back.

Positive thinking. Know that health can be regained. Believe and know that it can be done. Notice how many successful men and women are positive thinkers. The body obeys the brain and when you believe something all the natural elements of your body help to make it so. The magic formula through which it does manifest is *FAITH, BELIEF*. We all have different degrees of faith. The Bible says "according to your faith be it unto you."

Our bodies are not as yet adjusted to a sedentary form of life. Atrophy sets in if we fail to use our bodies. Improper foods can also cause disease. Proper foods cure disease. Remember, nature does the real healing utilizing the natural defenses of the body.

HEALTH QUOTES

Health is a gift, but you have to work to keep it.

—Hubbard

Have a happy loving attitude. A positive attitude is mature health. This is the best state of physiological, and spiritual health that can be obtained on this earth.

—Dr. Norman Beals

The only way for a rich man to be healthy is by exercise and abstinence, to live as if he were poor.

—Sir William Temple

But health is not merely a matter of the body. Anger, hatred, grief, and fear are among the influences most destructive of vitality.

—Dr. Richardson

The length of our stay in this world may depend to a great extent upon the judgment we exercise in the care of our body. By careful attention and moderation we can live longer and better.

—A. A. M.

SUGGESTED GOALS AND OBJECTIVES
In Planning Health

Well planned nutrition.

Exercise each day.

Control weight.

Better eating habits.

Eliminate prolonged anxiety.

Regular physical examination.

Regular dental examination.

Discipline and restraint over careless
and excessive habits.

Take a walk every day.

Rest and relaxation.

Play golf each week.

Learn to bowl.

Plan weekend trips.

Plan vacation.

Continuous energy and enthusiasm.

HEALTH TIPS

Living longer means little unless the extra years are healthy, active ones. The added years that modern medicine has given you can be good ones if you practice a little moderation and follow these simple steps:

You can keep young in spirit, body, and mind if . . .

You see your family physician regularly for a physical checkup. He can diagnose and treat successfully almost any ailment if he finds it early enough.

Watch your diet. As the years pass usually less food is required. You will need more protein, vitamins and fluids but fewer fats and calories. If you need to lose weight, let your doctor guide you.

Get adequate rest. Your mind and body need peace and quiet, to recoup from the rigors of the day. Know your limitations and avoid over-exertion and strain, both physically and mentally.

Pursue physical exercise. Keep your body parts in good working order by using them . . . by mowing the lawn, taking a brisk walk or swim, or playing a round of golf.

Fill your days with productivity. The quickest way to "old age" is through boredom. Keep up your interest in your work and your surroundings. Participate in community affairs—be a doer—share your time and talents.

Prepare for the future. Worry is a shortcut to "old age"—it can even lead to illness. Many worries about tomorrow can be avoided if you plan and budget for future financial needs with adequate insurance and savings programs.

—Dr. Charles W. Mayo

HEALTH QUESTIONNAIRE

Health is our greatest resource. It is the basis not only of
efficiency, but also of human happiness. To have good physical
health we must train ourselves and acquire good health habits.
It is our responsibility to give our magnificent human body the
highest and best care.

When we feel good we are enthusiastic, and have plenty of energy.
We can carry forward our workload and all the extra things we want
to do, inorder to enlarge and enjoy our life. Obtaining and main-
taining optimum health should be our number one goal.

Are you taking good care of your body?_____
Are there things you are doing now, which do not contribute to good
health? What are they? How do you plan to correct them? _____
_____
_____
_____
_____

What improvements do you need to make in your eating habits?_____
_____
_____
_____

Do you get plenty of exercise each day?_____
How can you improve your schedule to include walking, swimming, golf
and other exercise?_____
_____
_____

Do you make good use of your leisure time? Do you have physical
work to do at home, either hobby, or house improvement, or gardening
to help relieve the tension of a sedentary life?_____
_____
_____
_____

Do you get ample sleep?_____
Do you have plenty of variety in your activities to ward off fatigue
caused by boredom?_____

Are you overweight? How can you get your weight down? List the
things you can do to improve this condition._____
_____

What bad habits do you want to overcome? (Smoking, excessive drinking, lack of sleep, improper eating, list them)._____
_____

Describe the state of health you would like to have and then list
the things you can do to attain this state of health._____
_____
_____
_____

Moderation is health - excess is disease.

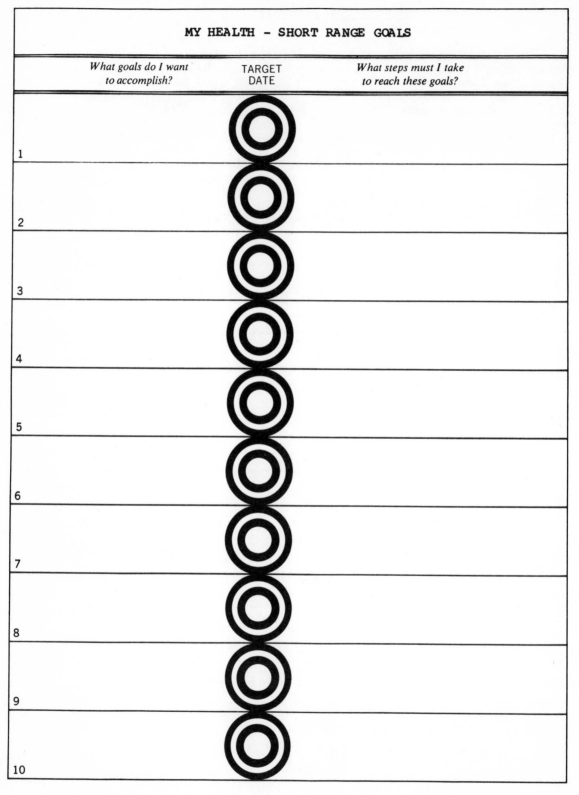

MY HEALTH – SHORT RANGE GOALS

What goals do I want to accomplish?	TARGET DATE	*What steps must I take to reach these goals?*
1		
2		
3		
4		
5		
6		
7		
8		
9		
10		

146

MY HEALTH – LONG RANGE GOALS

	What goals do I want to accomplish?	TARGET DATE	*What steps must I take to reach these goals?*
1			
2			
3			
4			
5			
6			
7			
8			
9			
10			

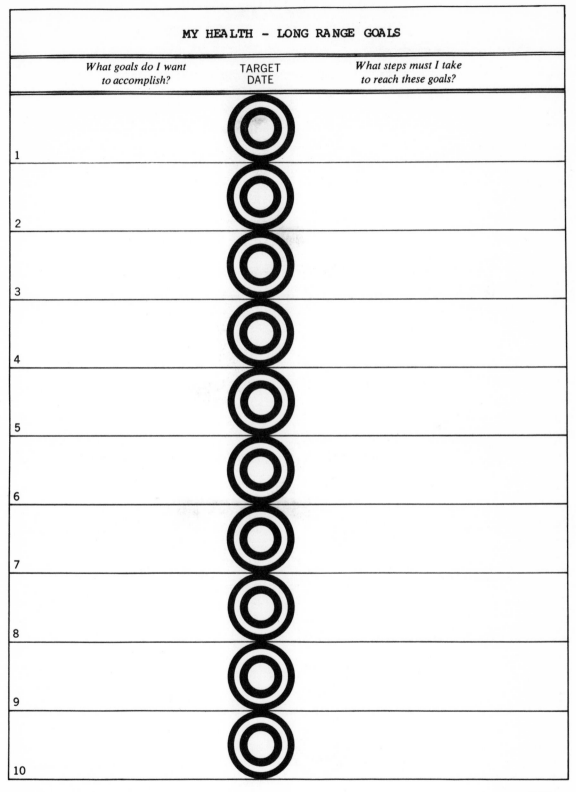

147

MY PLAN

What do I really want to accomplish? _____

_____

_____

_____

_____

_____

What is the most effective and expedient way of reaching my goal? _____

_____

_____

_____

_____

_____

I have the following abilities, skills, and knowledge for achieving this goal: _____

_____

_____

_____

_____

Additional information, skills, and abilities needed: _____

_____

_____

_____

_____

Here are the places I will go, the people I will see, the sources I will use, to help me gain new knowledge, skills and abilities I need: _____

_____

_____

_____

_____

_____

The first step I will take this week: _____

_____

_____

My next main steps will be as follows (Include deadlines): _____

_____

_____

_____

_____

My target date for reaching this goal: _____

MY SPECIFIC PLAN

What do I really want to accomplish?

TARGET DATE FOR COMPLETION

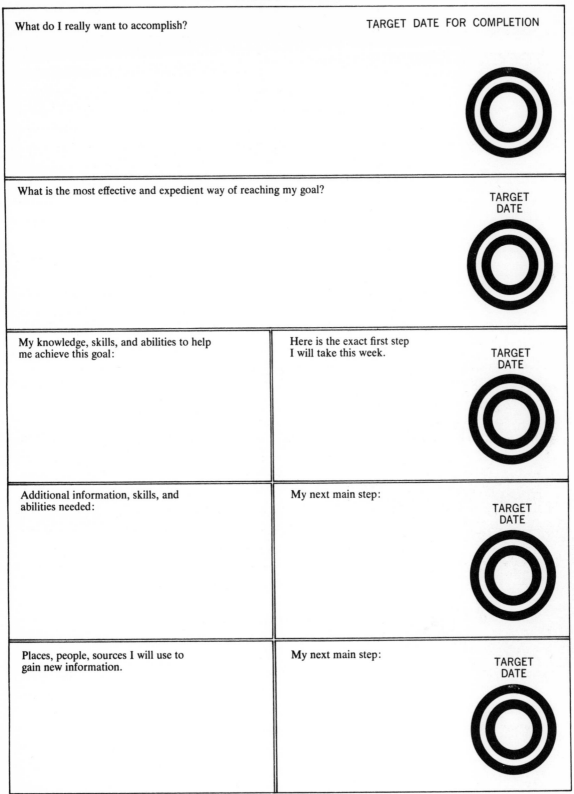

What is the most effective and expedient way of reaching my goal?

TARGET
DATE

My knowledge, skills, and abilities to help me achieve this goal:

Here is the exact first step
I will take this week.

TARGET
DATE

Additional information, skills, and abilities needed:

My next main step:

TARGET
DATE

Places, people, sources I will use to gain new information.

My next main step:

TARGET
DATE

CONSTRUCTIVE THINKING

Here is the crux, the core of life — "As a man thinketh, so is he." So simple, but how true, how profound. How few understand and practice this natural law.

Man is great or small, according to the way he thinks and limits himself. Learn to take the ceilings off your limitations.

To consciously think that "I CAN" impels the subconscious faculties into action. This principle is the genesis of all successful men.

A Natural Law of Life:—AS YOU THINK SO YOU ARE

Do you know that if you were to build an electronic computer to equal the human brain it would cost over a billion dollars, and then it would not be complete.

Man must learn how to use his billion dollar equipment. Do you fully realize how wonderfully you are made? Do you realize the wonderful equipment you have? Do you use it properly, or do you misuse it?

Most of us are careless with our thoughts. We do not realize the importance of thoughts to proper and efficient living. You are the sum total of your thoughts. You become what you think about. You move toward what you dwell upon. Thoughts mold us. You will never be any higher or better than your best thoughts. Everything starts with a thought—buildings, bridges, airplanes, rockets, you name it. The greatest statue Michelangelo carved started with a thought.

You put food into your body for physical growth and nourishment. You put thoughts into your mind to live by. Thoughts become your life. Thoughts become what you do. Thoughts become what you are. Thoughts become you.

What do the wise men say about thoughts? One of the wisest men who ever lived was Marcus Aurelius, and he said: "A man's life is what his thoughts make it." The Bible says: "As a man thinketh so is he . . . Whatsoever things are true, honest, just, pure, lovely, of good report, think on these things."

Dr. John Schindler in his famous book "How To Live 365 Days A Year," mentioned the fact that the biggest percentage of sick people who came to see him had illnesses that were caused by improper thoughts. He calls it "emotionally induced illness." You can make yourself sick by thinking the wrong thoughts.

What are the different kinds of thoughts? There are many kinds of thoughts. Thoughts can be: constructive or destructive, pleasant or depressed, positive or negative, good or bad. Now here is the important fact. "The thoughts you place in your mind determine what you are." Thoughts shape one's life. Thoughts determine success or failure in one's work, study, and daily living. Thoughts are the bridge to success or the bridge to failure. Each of us must live off the fruit of his own thoughts.

Let us analyze what we do in our mind with a thought. Our mind is like the soil—the thought we put into our mind is the seed. Whatever we plant will grow. If we plant potatoes in the soil we grow potatoes, not wheat. If we plant poison we will likewise grow poison. Whatever seed or thought we plant in our mind will likewise grow. If we plant negative thoughts we have negative results. If we plant depressed thoughts we will harvest depressed results.

If we plant bad thoughts we will harvest only bad. This is a law as real as the Law of Gravity. Right thoughts produce success, improper thoughts produce failure. Pleasant thoughts are conducive to happiness and good health. Your brain can work for you or against you, depending on how you control it.

Here is another illustration. Your mind is like a television camera. The picture is taken of each of your thoughts and each picture is filed away in your mind, in a memory cell, which the scientists call a neuron. The human brain has 100 billion neurons or memory cells. If you fill your brain with negative or improper thoughts it stands to reason that you will become negative in your thinking.

Improper negative thoughts sink people. Example: A ship can sail on water all around the world, many, many times, but just let enough water get into the ship and it will sink. Just so with the human mind. Let enough negative thoughts or improper thoughts get into the human mind and the person sinks just like the ship. You must control your thoughts, as well as your actions. The only person who can hurt you is *YOU*.

Psychology has already taught us that destructive thoughts can be forced out of our minds simply by substituting good ones for bad. "As a man thinketh in his heart so is he." Psychology has also shown us that if we allow worry, fear, or abnormal anxiety to stay in our minds, the brain cannot function smoothly, and its maladjustment affects the entire nervous system of which it is the center, a system which operates in every part of the body.

The study of psychology has shown that the right attitude of mind toward life can be attained, but we must develop it. Technology (the application of science to industry) has made wonderful strides in improving things, and psychology may be able to do as much in helping man to properly use his mind.

William James, the famous American psychologist, said: *The greatest discovery of my generation is that human beings can alter their lives by altering their attitudes of mind.*

An enthusiastic man attracts enthusiasm from others. Faith attracts faith. Courage attracts courage. Confidence attracts confidence. Optimism attracts optimism. Trust attracts trust. Love attracts love. Belief attracts belief. Action attracts action. Success attracts success. It is the natural law of attraction . . . like attracts like.

The principle: You move toward that upon which you dwell. You tend to become like that about which you think most vividly, most repeatedly, most intensively, and most imaginatively.

EXAMINE YOUR BELIEFS

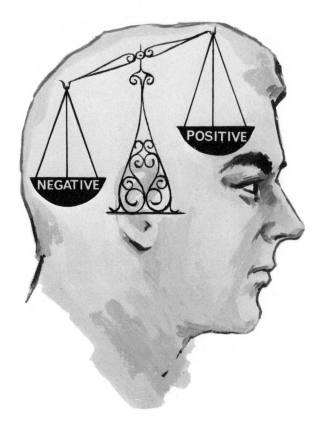

If you visualize a failure you tend to create the conditions that produce failure. Your body obeys your mind.

MEN DO NOT PLAN TO FAIL . . . THEY FAIL TO PLAN. Most men fail because they do not have a sound philosophy or plan of life. Their resulting failure was created by a mental attitude of disbelief or closed mindedness toward the need for a sound philosophy or plan of life in order to succeed.

The power to create thoughts, provided man by his Creator, is
a force by which man controls his life. Each day we need good
thoughts to live by.

Mind is the power that controls and governs everything, but man is a
conscious, thinking reasoning being, and can control the action of his
mind, hence may arise to the highest pinnacle of right-thinking and
achievement, and therefore be the arbiter of his own destiny.

—Walter Matthews

CONSTRUCTIVE THINKING

Albert Schweitzer, the great doctor and Nobel prize winner, was asked "What is wrong with men today?" His reply was "Men simply don't think."

Each of us is responsible for the development of our mental powers. Our mind is our kingdom of opportunities. Our minds come to us as standard equipment at birth. It's free, and we place little value on things that are given to us for nothing.

The mind, like life itself, is as unfathomable as God. Shakespeare makes one of his characters say, *Tis the mind that makes the body rich.* The mind and memory are the builders of wealth or poverty. It is the one place where thieves do not break in and steal.

The first quality of the mind is good sense. To have good sense is to be able to discern the dividing line between the true and the false, the just and the unjust, the excessive and the moderate, by means of an insight so sudden that it functions like one of the senses.

The supreme good of man according to all the sages, lies in refining his act of judgment to the highest degree of purity, in learning to think properly, and in cultivating a good mind, since all our misfortunes are born of our inability to make the proper choices.

Who knows what we can do until we have unleashed the full power of our faith, belief, and confidence in our own abilities.

Professor William James states, "Your belief at the beginning of a doubtful undertaking is the one thing that insures the successful outcome of your venture." This is always true when our mental attitude is solidly anchored by enthusiasm, observation, imagination, optimism, ambition, initiative, courage, confidence, purpose and persistence.

The road to accomplishment is to acquire the right thinking, and many teachers stress the use of affirmations as a means of conditioning ourselves. This proper mental attitude is necessary not only in matters of health, but is necessary to material or financial well-being.

The individual's ability to attain great success is limited only by the strength of his desires and belief in himself. "All things are possible to him that believeth."

As the fruits and flowers spring from their seeds, so do our characters develop from the thoughts implanted in our minds. A noble character is the result of noble thoughts.

> *Nurture your mind with great thoughts.*
> —Disraeli

Success or failure is caused more by our "mental attitudes" than by our "mental capacities." The accurate thinker examines the sources of his information, weighs statements for motivations, and tests their reasonableness.

There is only one thing which will really train the human mind and that is the voluntary use of the mind by the man himself. You may aid him, you may guide him, you may suggest to him, and above all you may inspire him; but the only thing worth having is that which he gets by his own exertions; and what he gets is proportionate to the effort he puts into it.

—A. Lawrence Lowell

THE BRIDGE YOU'LL NEVER CROSS

It's what you think that makes the world
    Seem dull or bright to you;
Your mind may color all things gray,
    Or make them radiant hue.

Be glad today, be true and wise,
    Seek gold amid the dross;
Waste neither time nor thought about
    The bridge you'll never cross.

There's useful work for you to do
    With hand and brain and heart;
There's urgent human service, too
    In which to take your part.

Make every opportunity
    A gain and not a loss;
The best is your's so do not fear
    The bridge you'll never cross.

If life seems drab and difficult,
    Just face it with a will;
You do not have to work alone
    Since God is with you still.

Press on with courage toward the goal,
    With truth your shield emboss;
Be strong, look up and just ignore
    The bridge you'll never cross.
                —Grenville Kleiser

It's your attitude that counts!

Happiness depends not on things around me, but on my attitude.
Everything in my life will depend upon my attitude.

MENTAL ATTITUDE

Every human being is faced with problems—worry—fear. The men and women who get the most out of life are those who habitually maintain their thinking on a high level. When problems arise, we must learn how to lift our thoughts to meet them. Keep your thoughts on a high plane and you will rise above your troubles.

Worry is brought on by the individual himself. It is perfectly normal to be concerned, but there is a big difference between worry and concern. Worry is like putting sand in the gears. Worry never cured anything, never dried a tear. It is unbelief, the opposite of faith. You are insecure only in your own mind.

Fear is our next villain. Fear can kill you like a bullet, only it takes longer depending on how long you like to suffer. Fear of falling off a ladder or some legitimate fear is normal. Many people are afraid to live and afraid to die. Their fears are self-created, or magnified. Marasmus is the wasting away of life, the ability each one of us has to think ourselves to death. Mental gangrene, discouraged, beaten down, morale low, the rust of life. Your attitudes affect your body.

Negative thinking, fear, worry, envy, jealousy, hatred, and greed are the mortal enemies of mankind. Psychiatry and psychoanalysis are plans or systems for seeking out mental monkey wrenches which have played havoc in the machinery of the human frame. The end result is accomplished only when a thought is changed.

It is much better to discover a way of life which needs no mental mending, and in which proper thoughts naturally flourish and triumph. Right mental attitude is the quality of mind which gives power to one's thoughts and plans. It is in our own minds that we conquer or submit to problems.

When feeling depressed, think over all the things you can that might cause that feeling. Then when you can see what it is, arrive at a solution to correct it. Usually it is some little thing—but it is like a little stone in your shoe. The stone is very small but it paralyzes your complete walking faculties.

"I can do all things through Christ which strengtheneth me." Repeat it the last thing before you fall asleep at night and the first thing on opening your eyes in the morning. The subconscious mind is very susceptible at those two periods. It will get into the subconscious and work with you, making you positive and creative.

Success is not an accident. Flooding the mind with positive suggestions is an established mental procedure with successful men and women in every walk of life.

SUGGESTED GOALS AND OBJECTIVES
For Your Mental Planning

Develop a cheerful, optimistic, positive attitude.

Write out and use my affirmations each day.

Be interested in others, let every one I meet feel that I regard them as a person of importance.

Have an attitude of expecting the best, to win the award, the job, etc. Act like a winner and become a winner.

This is going to be the best year of my life.

I will control my anger and passion of mind.

I will be calm and pleasant beginning right now.

Learn to eat problems for breakfast.

Conquer worry, develop an attitude of active concern.

I will control my thinking as carefully as I control my actions.

I will be optimistic, planning and expecting the best.

I will always dismiss from my mind immediately, all unpleasant and negative thoughts.

Thinking is only a process of talking to oneself intelligently. I talk to myself all the time, therefore, I will be careful what I say.

God is my strength and my refuge. There is not a problem, that together we cannot handle.

MENTAL QUOTES

There is one thing over which each person has absolute, inherent control, and that is his mental attitude.

—Clement Stone

For the best health and success, the outlook upon life must be cheerful, optimistic, buoyant and hopeful.

—Councillor

Success is ninety-nine percent mental attitude. It calls for love, joy, optimism, confidence, serenity, poise, faith, courage, cheerfulness, imagination, initiative, tolerance, honesty, humility, patience and enthusiasm.

—Wilfred Peterson

We must first realize in our thoughts the existence that we would attain in actual life. The three steps to enjoying a healthy mind are: (1) The control of anger and passion of mind. (2) The conquest of fear. (3) The elimination of worry.

—Councillor

Quiet minds cannot be perplexed or frightened, but go on in fortune and misfortune at their own private pace, like a clock during a thunderstorm.

—R. L. Stevenson

MENTAL LIFE QUESTIONNAIRE

A law of life: - "As you think so you are." Mind is the master power that moulds and makes man. The power of the mind is tremendous. Every act of man springs from the hidden seed of thought. Life is made or marred by our habitual thinking. Man, in the final analysis, is but the incarnation of his thoughts.

A mind can clearly formulate a plan when it is filled with constructive confident thoughts. A successful life starts with your good thoughts.

Thoughts lead on to purposes, purposes go forth in action; actions form habits; habits decide character; and character fixes our destiny.

--Tryon Edwards

Am I growing mentally every day of my life? How?_____
_____
_____

What can I do to improve myself so I am growing mentally and am more alert each day?_____
_____
_____

Do I guard my thoughts like I do my actions?_____
_____
_____

Do I always entertain thoughts that are cheerful, wholesome, positive? Thoughts of hope, faith, courage and success? (There is no medicine so potent as the right mental attitude)_____
_____
_____
_____

Do I think success, talk success, act success?_____
_____
_____

Can I create a clear mental picture of what I want to be, do? Successful men use their imaginations._____
_____
_____
_____

What can I do today to improve my mental attitude?_____
_____
_____
_____
_____
_____

An attitude is stronger than a fact.

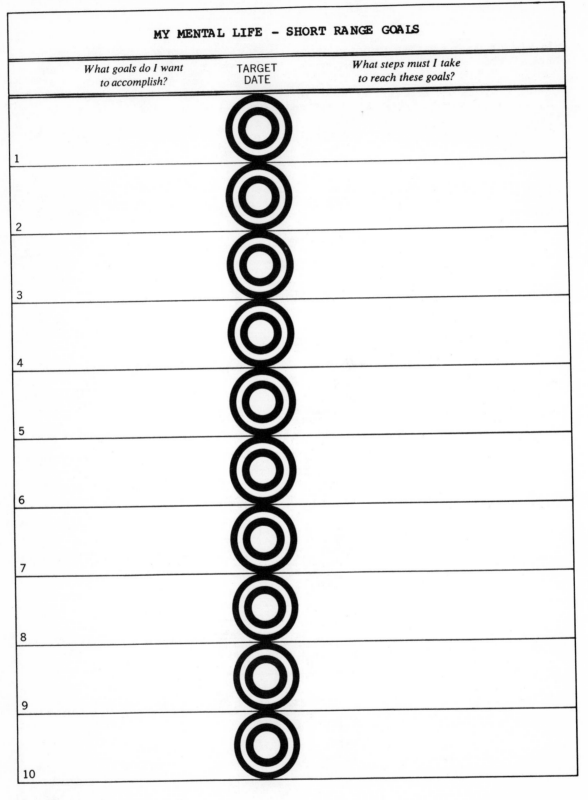

MY MENTAL LIFE – SHORT RANGE GOALS

What goals do I want to accomplish?	TARGET DATE	What steps must I take to reach these goals?
1		
2		
3		
4		
5		
6		
7		
8		
9		
10		

162

MY MENTAL LIFE - LONG RANGE GOALS

	What goals do I want to accomplish?	TARGET DATE	*What steps must I take to reach these goals?*
1			
2			
3			
4			
5			
6			
7			
8			
9			
10			

MY PLAN

What do I really want to accomplish? _____

_____

_____

_____

_____

_____

What is the most effective and expedient way of reaching my goal? _____

_____

_____

_____

_____

_____

I have the following abilities, skills, and knowledge for achieving this goal: _____

_____

_____

_____

_____

Additional information, skills, and abilities needed: _____

_____

_____

_____

_____

Here are the places I will go, the people I will see, the sources I will use, to help me gain new knowledge, skills and abilities I need: _____

_____

_____

_____

_____

The first step I will take this week: _____

_____

My next main steps will be as follows (Include deadlines): _____

_____

_____

_____

_____

My target date for reaching this goal: _____

MY SPECIFIC PLAN

What do I really want to accomplish?

TARGET DATE FOR COMPLETION

What is the most effective and expedient way of reaching my goal?

TARGET
DATE

My knowledge, skills, and abilities to help me achieve this goal:

Here is the exact first step
I will take this week.

TARGET
DATE

Additional information, skills, and abilities needed:

My next main step:

TARGET
DATE

Places, people, sources I will use to gain new information.

My next main step:

TARGET
DATE

Section Seven

FAMILY and HOME

What makes a home? Love and sympathy and confidence. The memories of childhood, the kindness of parents, they bring hopes of youth, the sisters' pride, the brothers' sympathy and help, the mutual confidence, the common hopes and interests and sorrows; these create and sanctify the home.

—JOHN LUBBOCK

THE HOME AND THE HOME EXECUTIVE

A home, in the first place, is not merely walls of wood, stone, or brick and mortar. A home is the center of our tenderest and purest affections, the atmosphere of true love, the haven where our souls find quietness and rest, the sanctuary of our loftiest ideals. It is the hearthstone of a happy and prosperous family. Home is the enjoyment of life at its best, the realization of the fondest hope, memories and joys and sometimes suffering never to be forgotten. Home is the palace where father is king and mother is queen.

The home is our greatest institution. The place where plastic youth is moulded into the finished product of citizenship. History shows that our national life never sinks below the home level and never rises above it. Unfortunately, the American home is becoming merely a lodging place, and is deteriorating. This is the case especially in the larger cities. So many children grow up without a real home.

"What is your occupation?" is a question one frequently hears asked by a quiz master on a radio or television program. If the person being questioned happens to be a lady she will answer apologetically, "Oh, just a housewife."

Instead of hanging her head apologetically she should lift it proudly and proclaim: "Mine is the greatest of all occupations. I am a home executive: I am making a home, building a marriage, bearing and mothering children. I am a molder of character, the builder of nations, empires and kingdoms. I am a producer and inspirer of men without which not even God can work out His purpose in the earth."

Now, having paid this high compliment to womanhood in general, and to mothers specifically, we might add that the compliment can only apply to a certain kind of mother. The mere fact that a woman bears a child does not make her either sacred, successful or invaluable. Bearing a child only fulfills a purely physical function common to the entire animal kingdom.

She demonstrates her value to her child and to society by what she is prior to the birth of her child, and what she does after his birth. Her character guarantees the child a good start in life and the kind of home environment she builds for her child, all things being equal, is society's hope of good and great men and women for the future.

There is no such thing as a decent society without good women. National leaders, armies, navies, educators, and law enforcement agencies may as well throw in the sponge when women generally lose their vision.

Every Family Should Have. . . .

There are a few essentials every family should have. These eleven items are "musts" for all of us.

A DOCTOR. A family physician who knows not only the members of the family personally, but also their medical records, is a source of great satisfaction. In the event of a family emergency, he'll usually be able to act quickly, without needless delay, without having to ask countless questions. It's a good idea to have the whole family checked each year.

A CLERGYMAN. Primarily, he guides us in our search for a basic faith by which to live. Also, every one of us has moments when we need the kind of help a minister, priest, or rabbi can give. Whether it be a personal problem, a misunderstanding within the family or outside, or other trouble, it's comforting to know there's someone to whom to turn in confidence for help.

A HOUSEHOLD INVENTORY. If your home burned down tomorrow, could you produce for the insurance company an itemized list of your belongings? If not, you might have difficulty collecting more than a fraction of the value of what you thought you had before its destruction. An accurate inventory also tells you and your agent how much insurance you ought to carry on your household goods.

When making a list of your things, write down the amount paid for each item and the date bought. Go through every room in the house; garage, too. Your insurance agent will give you a handy little booklet in which to record the information gathered. Bring the list up to date once a year.

A CHECKING ACCOUNT. Hardly a need to remind you of the value of this one. Cancelled checks not only give you a record of what you've spent your money for; they're also proof of your having paid a certain bill. They're much safer than cash through the mail, and they provide a record that's almost priceless at income-tax-paying time.

168

A PETTY CASH CONTAINER. Seems like there's always a need for small change around the house—for the paper boy, bus fare, an extra bottle of milk at the corner grocery, and countless other items. Many families find it useful to have a bowl in a convenient place with enough nickels, dimes, quarters, half-dollars, even a dollar bill or two, to handle such things. Caution: put everyone on his honor to make replacement.

A SAVINGS PROGRAM. Looking ahead to the time of retirement, even though that may be years away, it's good to start soon on a systematic program of saving. The amount saved each year is not so important as developing the habit of setting aside something at regular intervals, say, every month, every six months, or annually. It's one of those things you'll be mighty grateful for one day.

A SAFETY DEPOSIT BOX. The cost is minor, actually a few cents per week, but having it will protect you against loss of important documents like savings bonds, insurance policies, stock certificates, marriage and birth certificates, deed to the house, etc. You might even put seldom-used jewelry there.

HOME SAFE. Some families keep their precious possessions and records in a UL approved fireproof safe at home. This is the most convenient way.

REFERENCE BOOKS. If you're going to even begin to answer the children's questions, better have on hand a good desk dictionary, an up-to-date world atlas, an almanac (book of facts), a good encyclopedia, and, yes, a book of quotations. They make good Christmas presents for the family, and the cost of each is not excessive. Keep them handy for immediate reference. They'll be used, often.

A WILL. It reminds you of unpleasant things, but it's very important. Without a will your property may not be distributed as you'd like, and taxes may take an unnecessarily large chunk. For your own satisfaction, and for the protection of your loved ones, have a will drawn by an attorney, and put it in your safety deposit box or safe. It's a good idea to review it, say, every five years.

PLANNING WITH THE FAMILY. Whether it be where to go on the next vacation trip, when to pay off the home mortgage, or how to finance the children's education, make it a family project. Get every family member in on it, including the youngsters. Ask for ideas. Discuss each one. If you're planning a weekend jaunt, assign someone to recommend the route to take, another one to suggest where to stay overnight, and so forth.

OUR CHILDREN

NAME: _____ Born _____ Place _____
  Married to: _____ Birthday _____
   Address: _____
    _____ Phone _____ Anniversary _____
  Their Children: (1) _____ Birthday _____
               (2) _____ Birthday _____
               (3) _____ Birthday _____

NAME: _____ Born _____ Place _____
  Married to: _____ Birthday _____
   Address: _____
    _____ Phone _____ Anniversary _____
  Their children: (1) _____ Birthday _____
               (2) _____ Birthday _____
               (3) _____ Birthday _____

NAME: _____ Born _____ Place _____
  Married to: _____ Birthday _____
   Address: _____
    _____ Phone _____ Anniversary _____
  Their Children: (1) _____ Birthday _____
               (2) _____ Birthday _____
               (3) _____ Birthday _____

NAME: _____ Born _____ Place _____
  Married to: _____ Birthday _____
   Address: _____
    _____ Phone _____ Anniversary _____
  Their Children: (1) _____ Birthday _____
               (2) _____ Birthday _____
               (3) _____ Birthday _____

OTHER DEPENDENT CHILDREN:

NAME: _____ Birthday _____
Address: _____

NAME: _____ Birthday _____
Address: _____

HUSBAND'S FAMILY

PARENTS

Father_____

      Birthdate_____Birth Place_____Died_____

      Address_____

_____

Mother_____Maiden Name_____

      Birthdate_____Birth Place_____Died_____

      Address_____

_____

BROTHERS AND SISTERS

Name_____Birthdate _____

Address_____Phone_____

Marital Status_____Anniversary_____

Spouse's Name_____Birthday_____

  Their Children_____Birthday_____

_____Birthday_____

_____Birthday_____

Name_____Birthdate _____

Address_____Phone_____

Marital Status_____Anniversary _____

Spouse's Name_____Birthday_____

  Their Children_____Birthday_____

_____Birthday_____

_____Birthday_____

Name_____Birthdate_____

Address_____Phone_____

Marital Status_____Anniversary_____

Spouse's Name_____Birthday_____

  Their Children_____Birthday_____

_____Birthday_____

_____Birthday_____

Name_____Birthdate_____

Address_____Phone_____

Marital Status_____Anniversary_____

Spouse's Name_____Birthday_____

  Their Children_____Birthday_____

_____Birthday_____

_____Birthday_____

171

WIFE'S FAMILY

PARENTS

Father_____
        Birthdate_____Birth Place_____Died_____
        Address_____
        _____
Mother_____Maiden Name_____
        Birthdate_____Birth Place_____Died_____
        Address_____
        _____

BROTHERS AND SISTERS

Name_____Birthdate_____
Address_____Phone_____
Marital Status_____Anniversary_____
Spouse's Name_____Birthday_____
   Their Children_____Birthday_____
                 _____Birthday_____
                 _____Birthday_____

Name_____Birthdate_____
Address_____Phone_____
Marital Status_____Anniversary_____
Spouse's Name_____Birthday_____
   Their Children_____Birthday_____
                 _____Birthday_____
                 _____Birthday_____

Name_____Birthdate_____
Address_____Phone_____
Marital Status_____Anniversary_____
Spouse's Name_____Birthday_____
   Their Children_____Birthday_____
                 _____Birthday_____
                 _____Birthday_____

Name_____Birthdate_____
Address_____Phone_____
Marital Status_____Anniversary_____
Spouse's Name_____Birthday_____
   Their Children_____Birthday _____
                 _____Birthday _____
                 _____Birthday _____

OUR GRANDPARENTS

MY GRANDPARENTS:

	Father's Family	Mother's Family
Grandfather's Name	_____	_____
Birthplace	_____	_____
Dates	<u>Born</u> Died	<u>Born</u> Died
Grandmother's Name	_____	_____
Birthplace	_____	_____
Dates	<u>Born</u> Died	<u>Born</u> Died

Their Address_____

Comments on their background, famous relations, accomplishments,etc

_____
_____
_____
_____

SPOUSES'S GRANDPARENTS:

	Father's Family	Mother's Family
Grandfather's Name	_____	_____
Birthplace	_____	_____
Dates	<u>Born</u> Died	<u>Born</u> Died
Grandmother's Name	_____	_____
Birthplace	_____	_____
Dates	<u>Born</u> Died	<u>Born</u> Died

Their Address_____

Comments on their background, famous relations, accomplishments,etc

_____
_____
_____
_____

OTHER RELATIONS WE KEEP IN CONTACT WITH

Name_____Relation_____
Address_____

Name_____Relation_____
Address_____

Name_____Relation_____
Address_____

OUR HOMES

Mid pleasures and palaces though we may roam,=
Be it ever so humble, there's no place like home;
A charm from the skies seems to hallow us there,
Which, sought through the world, is n'er met with
elsewhere.

--J. H. Payne

Street Address	City/State	Date Occupied	Date Moved	Remarks

OUR AUTOMOBILES

Make	Style & Model	Year Made	Purchased From	Date	Certificate of Title No.	Engine Number

174

IMPORTANT EVENTS

Trips, important persons met, anniversary celebrations, political events affecting our family, serious illnesses, operations, fires, unusual weather, great occasions, etc.

Person or Property	Event	Month-Day-Year

FAMILY SOCIAL SECURITY NUMBERS

Full Name	Number			Date Issued

BIRTHSTONES	and	FLOWERS	WEDDING ANNIVERSARIES
Garnet-onyx	Jan	Snowdrop	First - Paper
Ameythyst	Feb	Primrose	Second - Cotton
Bloodstone Aquamarine	Mar	Violet	Third - Leather
Diamond	Apr	Daisy	Fourth - Fruit-Flowers
Emerald	May	Hawthorn	Fifth - Wood
Pearl-Agate	Jun	Honeysuckle	Sixth - Candy
Ruby-Beryl	Jul	Water Lily	Seventh - Wool
Sardonyx Perizot	Aug	Poppy	Eighth - Pottery
Sapphire	Sep	Morning Glory	Ninth - Willow
Opal- Tourmaline	Oct	Hops	Tenth - Tin
Topaz	Nov	Chrysan- themum	Eleventh - Steel
Turquoise- Lapis-Lazuli	Dec	Holly	Twelfth - Silk & Linen

WEDDING ANNIVERSARIES

First - Paper
Second - Cotton
Third - Leather
Fourth - Fruit-Flowers
Fifth - Wood
Sixth - Candy
Seventh - Wool
Eighth - Pottery
Ninth - Willow
Tenth - Tin
Eleventh - Steel
Twelfth - Silk & Linen
Thirteenth - Lace
Fourteenth - Ivory
Fifteenth - Crystal
Twentieth - China
Twenty-Fifth - Silver
Thirtieth - Pearl
Fortieth - Ruby
Fiftieth - Gold
Fifty-Fifth - Emerald

WHOM TO NOTIFY

AT MOVING TIME

Post Office _____

Milk Man _____

Laundry _____

Telephone _____

Gas Company _____

Electric Company _____

Water Company _____

Banks _____

Insurance Agent _____

Investment Broker _____

Investments _____

Magazine Subscriptions _____

Newspaper Delivery _____

Alumni Association _____

Organizations _____

Employer _____

Schools _____

Motor Vehicles Dept. _____

Credit Cards _____

Charge Accounts _____

Library _____

Automobile Club _____

Gardener _____

Pool Maintenance _____

_____

_____

IN EVENT OF DEATH
Or Accident, Fire, or Theft

Attorney _____

Employer _____

Undertaker _____

Relatives _____

Will _____

Banks _____

Safe Deposit Box _____

Organizations _____

Selective Service _____

Military Reserve Unit _____

Cemetary Lots _____

Birth Certificate _____
Papers and Documents _____

Tax Records _____

Trust Funds _____

Investment Brokers _____

Accountant _____

Insurance Companies for:
Life Insurance _____

Health Insurance _____

Home Insurance _____
Home Contents Insurance _____

Personal Affects Insurance _____

Auto Insurance _____

Other _____

_____

_____

FAMILY AND HOME QUESTIONNAIRE

Is the atmosphere in your home loving and appreciate?_____

Are there things you can do to make it better?_____

Do members of your family respect and appreciate each other?_____

Are your children well-disciplined and well-mannered?_____

Do you have enough family activities to make you a well-knit group?

_____

Does each member have assigned tasks and duties for caring for the
home, cleaning, gardening, etc.? _____

Are there home or yard improvements that should be made?_____

Things to be fixed? _____

Do you want a new home?_____ Swimming pool?_____

If you have children of school age, how many years of formal education do you expect to give each child? _____

Child's Name	Grade School	High School	College	Trade School

What is the total amount of cash you will need over the years to
give each child a college education?_____

Do you carry enough life insurance, added to any capital you have,
to provide for your dependents in case of your death?_____

SUGGESTED GOALS AND OBJECTIVES

More loving, cooperative, peaceful atmosphere in our home.
Constant cheerfulness and enthusiasm.
Improve family discipline.
Schedule home improvements.
Plan better vacations.
Take more weekend trips together.
Plan camping, hiking, boating, fishing, hunting, etc.
Equipment and improvements we would like to have - swimming pool,
patio, bar-b-que, workshop, air-conditioning, additional room,
beach house, mountain cabin, boat.

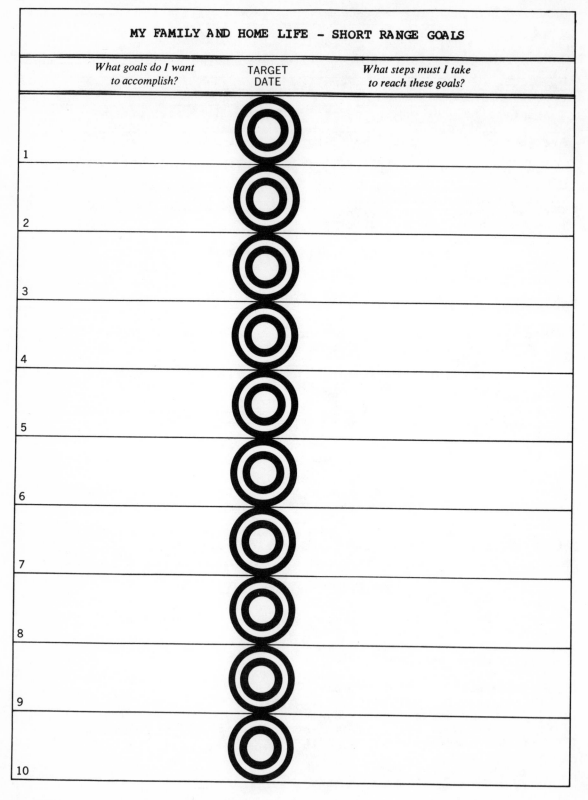

MY FAMILY AND HOME LIFE — SHORT RANGE GOALS

What goals do I want to accomplish?	TARGET DATE	*What steps must I take to reach these goals?*
1		
2		
3		
4		
5		
6		
7		
8		
9		
10		

178

MY FAMILY AND HOME LIFE – LONG RANGE GOALS

What goals do I want to accomplish?	TARGET DATE	What steps must I take to reach these goals?
1		
2		
3		
4		
5		
6		
7		
8		
9		
10		

MY PLAN

What do I really want to accomplish? _____

_____

_____

_____

_____

_____

_____

What is the most effective and expedient way of reaching my goal? ____

_____

_____

_____

_____

_____

I have the following abilities, skills, and knowledge for achieving this goal: ____

_____

_____

_____

_____

Additional information, skills, and abilities needed: _____

_____

_____

_____

_____

Here are the places I will go, the people I will see, the sources I will use, to help me gain new knowledge, skills and abilities I need: _____

_____

_____

_____

_____

_____

The first step I will take this week: _____

_____

My next main steps will be as follows (Include deadlines): _____

_____

_____

_____

_____

_____

My target date for reaching this goal: _____

MY SPECIFIC PLAN

What do I really want to accomplish?

TARGET DATE FOR COMPLETION

What is the most effective and expedient way of reaching my goal?

TARGET DATE

My knowledge, skills, and abilities to help me achieve this goal:

Here is the exact first step I will take this week.

TARGET DATE

Additional information, skills, and abilities needed:

My next main step:

TARGET DATE

Places, people, sources I will use to gain new information.

My next main step:

TARGET DATE

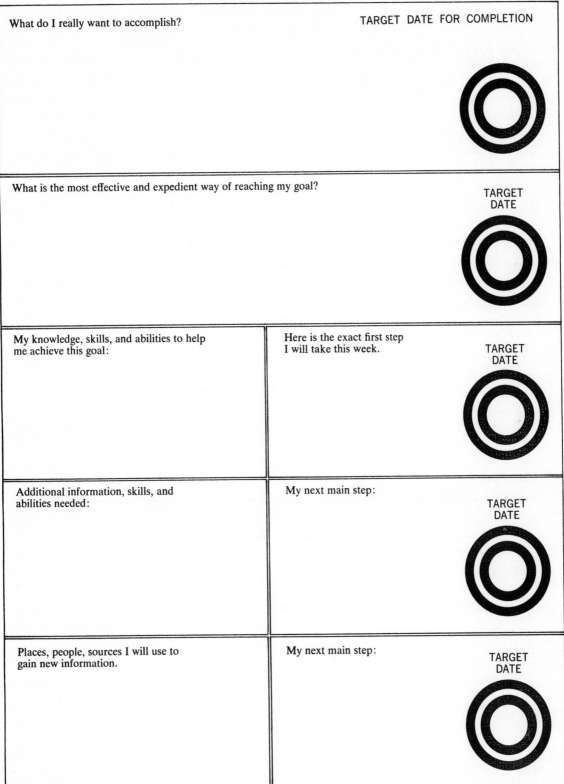

Section Eight

TRAVEL and CULTURE

Before I started on my trip around the world someone gave me one of the most valuable hints I have ever had. It consists merely in shutting your eyes when you are in the midst of a great moment, or close to some marvel of time or space, and convincing yourself that you are at home again with the experience over and past; and what would you wish most to have examined or done if you could turn time and space back again.

—WILLIAM BEEBE

TRAVEL

Travel provides a change of climate and scenery, which is often more necessary for certain ailments than medicine. Although travel may be considered the richest of all pleasures, it may also be considered a good investment.

—A. B. Zu Tavern

184

THE WORLD BELONGS TO HIM . . . WHO HAS SEEN IT!

Do you want to live some of your dreams? Imagine yourself . . . having your picture taken in front of the Eiffel Tower in Paris, St. Marks Square in Venice, the Colosseum in Rome, the Pyramids of Egypt, the Taj Mahal in India, the Statue of Liberty in New York Harbor.

Imagine yourself . . . standing amid the columns of the Acropolis, the city of Athens beneath you . . . wandering through the streets of Rome to St. Peters . . . walking down the boulevards of Paris—the Arc de Triomph or the Eiffel Tower before you . . . cheering at the opera in Milan, skiing at the Matterhorn . . . attending church in Westminster Abbey . . . meditating in the Sistine Chapel . . . boating up the Rhine.

It will be great to sip espresso at the Rue de La Paix, enjoy fettuchine at Alfredo's, pressed duck at the Tour d'Argent, beer at Tivoli Gardens, steak and kidney pie at the Cheshire Inn.

Travel educates and enlightens us by broadening our outlook on life in a way that cannot be learned from books. We may read the most vivid and accurate description, pour over maps and plans and pictures—and yet the reality will burst on us like a revelation. The actual sight gives life to the idea. If we have eyes to see, ears to hear, patience to understand—a whole new life is in store for you—through travel.

Travel can be purposeful . . . making it more fun than just passing time sight-seeing. You will receive so much more from the time and money you have invested if you make it a point to accomplish certain things during each trip you take—whether to Istanbul or to a national park.

If you have hobbies . . . collect things as you go. If you have a special cultural interest . . . broaden it as you go. If you have a special educational bent, learn what others are doing in this field in other countries. Consult with businessmen about your product or field of interest. Is there a product you can distribute, a method you can adapt, or an employee you can acquire?

Shopping tours of unusual and quaint shops are a highlight of any trip. If you have items you collect, special clothes you would like to have, or special gifts for friends, make a list of them and use it as a guide and conversation piece in the stores you visit.

To take the best advantage of all there is to see and do—set your own pace. Concentrate on countries and cities where you have the most to gain personally. Go where you want to go—be yourself—and you will learn more and enjoy more. We are all travelers on the highway of learning. By experience and observation we learn the fine art of living.

Specific things I want to see in (list country, and place, etc).

_____

_____

_____

_____

Restaurants, special holiday events, concerts, musicals, fiestas,
special affairs I want to be sure and enjoy:_____

_____

_____

_____

_____

People to see: friends, pen-pals, relatives, business contacts,
artists, entertainers, local people with special appeal: _____

_____

_____

_____

Native products and art objects I'd like to buy:_____

_____

_____

_____

_____

Travel gives a character of experience to our knowledge, and brings
the figures upon the table of memory into strong relief.
                                        --Henry T. Tuckerman

The advantages of travel last through life, and often as we sit at home some bright and perfect view of Venice, of Paris, London, Florence or Rome comes back to us with pleasant memories of days wisely spent in travel.

The Alps, the blue Mediteranean, the cities of Europe, with all their memories and treasures, are now brought within a few hours of us. Surely, no one who has the opportunity should hesitate to travel. The jet plane is the "silver bridge" to all countries of the world.

What places do I want to visit on my next trip?

Europe	United States	Alaska
Holy Land	South America	Canada
Egypt	Mexico	Australia
Africa	Hawaii	Orient
Asia		

When do I plan to take my next foreign trip?_____
Where will I go?_____
What mode of transportation shall I use?_____

Do I want to take a tour?_____Which one?_____
What are the departure dates?_____
What countries are included?_____
How much money will I need (including extra for food, shopping, clothes, etc)?_____
How will I meet this cost?_____
_____

Do I want to travel on my own?_____Where will I go?_____
_____
Shall I make reservations myself or use a travel service?_____
_____
_____

What special projects will I pursue while travelling?_____
_____
Preparations to make (time and item)_____
_____
_____
_____

What local trips would I like to take? _____
_____
Time schedule:_____Method of travel_____
Do I need reservations? Where?_____
_____
Preparations to make:_____
_____
_____
_____

MY TRAVEL PORTFOLIO
EUROPE

Trip planned for_____.
Had my picture taken at the
Big Ben
London on_____.

Trip planned for_____.
Had my picture taken at the
Eiffel Tower
Paris on_____.

Trip planned for_____.
Had my picture taken at the
Colosseum
Rome on_____.

Trip planned for_____.
Had my picture taken at the
Acropolis
Athens on_____.

Trip planned for_____.
Had my picture taken at the
Castles on the Rhine
Germany on_____.

Trip planned for_____.
Had my picture taken at the
Bull Fights
Spain on_____.

Trip planned for_____.
Had my picture taken at the
Matterhorn
Switzerland on_____.

Trip planned for_____.
Had my picture taken at the
Mermaid Statue
Copenhagen on_____.

When your travel plans have been fulfilled and you have
had your picture taken at these various places, you may
wish to paste your picture in the proper square.

188

MY TRAVEL PORTFOLIO
UNITED STATES

Trip planned for_____.
Had my picture taken at the
__Capitol Building__
Washington, on_____.
D.C.

Trip planned for_____.
Had my picture taken at the
__Niagara Falls__
__New York__ on_____.

Trip planned for_____.
Had my picture taken at the
__Statue of Liberty__
__New York__ on_____.

Trip planned for_____.
Had my picture taken at the
__New Orleans__
__Louisiana__ on_____.

Trip planned for_____.
Had my picture taken at the
__Grand Canyon__
__Arizona__ on_____.

Trip planned for_____.
Had my picture taken at the
__Golden Gate Bridge__
__San Fran-__ on_____.
cisco

Trip planned for_____.
Had my picture taken at the
__Independence Hall__
__Philadelphia On__ __.

Trip planned for_____.
Had my picture taken at the
__Mount Rushmore__
__So. Dakota__ on_____.

MY TRAVEL PORTFOLIO
ORIENT

Trip planned for_____.
Had my picture taken at the
Taj Mahal
India_____on_____.

Trip planned for_____.
Had my picture taken at the
Siam Temples
Bangkok___on_____.

Trip planned for_____.
Had my picture taken at the
Hong Kong
China_____on_____.

Trip planned for_____.
Had my picture taken at the
Mt. Fujiyama
Japan_____on_____.

Trip planned for_____.
Had my picture taken at the
Buddha of Kamakuru
Japan_____on_____.

Trip planned for_____.
Had my picture taken at the
Waikiki
Honolulu on_____.

Trip planned for_____.
Had my picture taken at the
Mosque of St. Sophia
Constanti- on_____.
nople

Trip planned for_____.
Had my picture taken at the
Bridge of Sydney
Australia on_____.

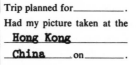

MY TRAVEL PORTFOLIO
OTHER TRIPS

Trip planned for_____.
Had my picture taken at the
Lake Louise
Canada on_____.

Trip planned for_____.
Had my picture taken at the
Capetown,
So.Africa on_____.

Trip planned for_____.
Had my picture taken at the
Game Reserve
Africa on_____.

Trip planned for_____.
Had my picture taken at the
Pyramids
Egypt on_____.

Trip planned for_____.
Had my picture taken at the
_____**Ruins**_____
Mexico on_____.

Trip planned for_____.
Had my picture taken at the
Christ of the Andes
So.America on_____.

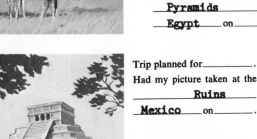

Trip planned for_____.
Had my picture taken at the
Babylon
Holy Land on_____.

Trip planned for_____.
Had my picture taken at the
Caribbean Islands
_____ on_____.

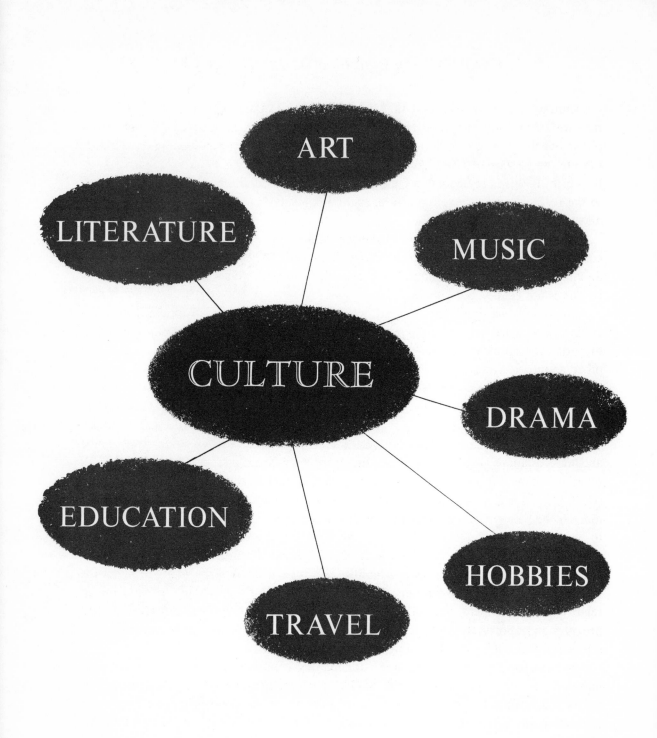

CULTURE—The Expression Of Our Greater Self

Culture is to know the best that has been said and thought in the world. If this is true we must study our great predecessors and learn from them. It is not knowledge per se but the right use of knowledge that can lead us out of our prevailing dilemma, to the utmost heights of abundant living. The Bible says man is to have dominion over the earth. If this is to become a fact, then it must start within you. You take the beauty to the rose, you must have the awareness and capacity to see and accept all the beauty and wonders that surround you.

Carlyle said: "The great law of culture: Let each become all that he was created capable of being." The late Somerset Maugham said: "The value of culture is its effect on character. It avails nothing unless it ennobles and strengthens that. Its use is for life. Its aim is not beauty, but goodness."

Man can have dominion over the world if he first rules himself by study and discipline. A widened view of life is possible by availing ourselves of the finest in literature, the arts, communications, technical knowledge, cultural knowledge of our land and other countries. Man must see himself still in a natural world where there is beauty, peace, trees, flowers, cycles of life and death, growth and decay. He must see mankind as essentially the same as it has always been with the same desires, aspirations, ambitions, follies and weaknesses.

He must be acquainted with practical philosophy; books that show up man's noble and base qualities; art that expresses the most inner yearnings of his heart and soul; religion which expresses man's searchings for a higher meaning. All these understandings will add to any man's value to himself, his company, and his community. The more technical society becomes the more cultured and inwardly directed we will need to be.

Our cultural pursuits can be a part of our general business activity; a means for sharing and spending time with our families and relatives; a way of getting to know the true character of our co-workers, customers, and associates. Taking a customer or relative to a light opera, a good play, or a concert, combines business and pleasure and provides an opportunity for making maximum use of our time. We grow culturally ourselves and fulfill a social obligation.

We should also plan leisure time—for reading great books, visiting art collections, museums, art auctions, enjoying the beauty of nature in surrounding parks, recreation areas, and resorts. If you are artistically or musically inclined it is a greater expression to develop these talents than to pursue others, for culture is the inward development of the best that is in us.

CHECKLIST OF CULTURAL ACTIVITIES

"To read a beautiful poem now and then, to witness a good play, to see a fine picture occasionally, to hear good music, is refreshing and stimulating as nothing else in life is. And it is always a wonderful thing to be able to create and interpret, to write, to paint, to play, and to sing, oneself."   --Councillor

Adult education courses and lectures to attend:
1. _____
2. _____
3. _____
4. _____
5. _____

Museums and Art Galleries to visit:
1. _____
2. _____
3. _____
4. _____
5. _____

Light Opera Season - This Years Attractions - Dates
1. _____
2. _____
3. _____
4. _____
5. _____

Symphony Season - Attractions - Dates
1. _____
2. _____
3. _____
4. _____
5. _____

Legitimate Theatre: Theatre - Announced Attractions - Dates
1. _____
2. _____
3. _____
4. _____
5. _____

Books - informative, inspiration books I want to read:
1. _____   6. _____
2. _____   7. _____
3. _____   8. _____
4. _____   9. _____
5. _____   10. _____

Subjects I want to expand in my personal library, books to buy.
1. _____   5. _____
2. _____   6. _____
3. _____   7. _____
4. _____   8. _____

194

CULTURAL QUESTIONNAIRE

Your true philosophy of life is revealed by what you do when you are free to do what you want to do. What do you like to do best with your spare time?_____
_____
_____
_____

Plan ways in which you can combine business, or family and social obligations with your cultural pursuits. List the possibilities.
_____
_____
_____
_____
_____

What kind of art, music, travel, plays, authors do you really like? What do you dislike?_____
_____
_____

What cultural activities have you wanted to engage in but have been putting off? How can you work them into your schedule now?
_____
_____

What talents and abilities do you have that will help you express yourself - what hobbies, crafts, musical instruments are you good at?_____
_____

What would you like to learn - is there a night school class in art, culture, world events, language, gourmet cooking, etc., that you would like to take? What schools teach it? How much time will it take? When are classes scheduled?_____
_____
_____
_____
_____

Could I cut down on the cocktail and barbeque parties without impairing my business, and do something more educational or instructive?_____
_____
_____
_____

Are there related fields to my business that I would like to know more about? Other sciences, languages, places to see? How can I schedule my time to include them?_____
_____
_____

What books am I reading?_____
_____
_____
_____
_____

What books do I want to read next? This year?_____
_____
_____
_____
_____

What theatres do I enjoy? When is the season? Have I planned
for season tickets? Who will I take with me?_____
_____
_____
_____

What museums, art galleries, theatres, music halls are in my city
that I haven't visited? When Do I plan to go?_____
_____
_____
_____
_____

Can I enhance my business or social standing by participating in
an art or theatre patrons group? Which one? What members do I
know?_____
_____
_____

Do I get out in natural surroundings enough? Where can I spend
my recreation time to get into the woods, or near water, to enjoy
nature and get the right perspective on my city life?_____
_____
_____
_____
_____

Do I surround myself with beauty? What art objects, paintings,
sculptures, antiques, would I like to have in my office, home,
study? Can the office lobby be improved with art objects or
displays?_____
_____
_____
_____
_____

Can I enhance the beauty of our home by attractive landscaping,
or other improvements?_____
_____
_____
_____

196

HOBBIES I WOULD LIKE TO PURSUE

A fascinating and creative interest apart from your work is an
absolute essential for happy living.
                                    --John Schindler,MD

No man is really happy or safe without a hobby, and it makes precious little difference what the outside interest may be - botany,
beetles, or butterflies; roses, tulips or irises; fishing, mount-
aineering or antiquities - anything will do so long as he straddles
it and rides it hard.
                                    --Sir William Osler,MD

Hobbies are without end. They are one of the most effective forms
of insurance against boredom of old age or the heavy artillery of
adversity. No man can afford to be without a hobby, and so long
as his hobbies are subordinate to his life work, the more hobbies
the better.
                                    --W. Beran Wolfe, PhD

I enjoy my trout fishing trips. But long ago, I learned that cat-
ching fish is the least important part of fishing. The thoughts
and moods and memories of a fishing trip are the really important
catch that one brings back creeled in memory to be lived again and
again. One goes back in memory to ramble aimlessly here and there
exploring secret places, climbing to the crest of a hill, following the course of a brook and experiencing again the thrill of the
battle royal with the big one that got away.
                                    --A. P. Gouthey

Hobbies I would like to pursue: _____
_____
_____

What do I already know about this subject? _____
_____
_____

What do I need to learn about this subject? _____
_____
_____

Books, manuals, guides, places to see, exhibits, experts to consult, personal contacts to make, friends with similar hobby, where
I can get help to start right: _____
_____
_____
_____

Necessary equipment and tools I'll need (include item, source,
cost, when needed): _____
_____
_____

I will work on this hobby: days of the week, hours: _____
_____

The hallmark of a cultured home has always been its library of worthwhile books. Books can fill gaps in formal education . . . . and enhance the knowledge of scholars. They set a person apart as one who has sought and tasted the wisdom of the ages.

Culture is the enlightenment or refinement of ourselves resulting from education or learning. It is the enlargement of one's mental horizon. It is not only of individual value but is also a bond among people of like tastes.

—Mary Alden Hopkins

SUGGESTED GOALS AND OBJECTIVES
For Your Cultural Development

Season tickets for opera, theatre.

Attend the best art exhibits.

Buy art objects for my home.

Study literature, master painters, languages.

Spend more time in natural surroundings.

Invite authors, musicians and art connisseurs to my home.

Read more books.

Plan a reading schedule.

Read a little in the classics each day for inspiration.

Take classes to develop my own creative abilities.

Join art groups if I already have a talent.

Learn more about gardening. Specialize on a particular type of garden or plant.

More time for present hobby.

Expand my knowledge of foods, gourmet cooking, wine tasting. Study, travel, read about cultures in other lands, especially those related to my business, family background, or hobbies.

Sponsor or participate in local theatre groups.

Find art objects in my travels.

Display local art in office reception rooms and lobby.

Find art and hobby talent among my employees and display their work. Have hobby show for the employees.

Expand my library.

Expand my record collection.

Travel more.

See countries I haven't been to.

Make definite schedule for my next trip.

See the United States.

Plan my vacation.

Plan a better schedule for my spare time activities.

Analyze my social activities and channel them into cultural pursuits to make better use of my time.

Plan time to just relax and meditate. Get acquainted with myself. Analyze who I really am and what I can really do.

We should endeavor to never let a day pass without adding something to our store of wisdom. Try to fix in your mind what is best in books, men, ideas and institutions.

Many times the reading of a book has made the fortune of a man—has decided his way in life.

—Ralph Waldo Emerson

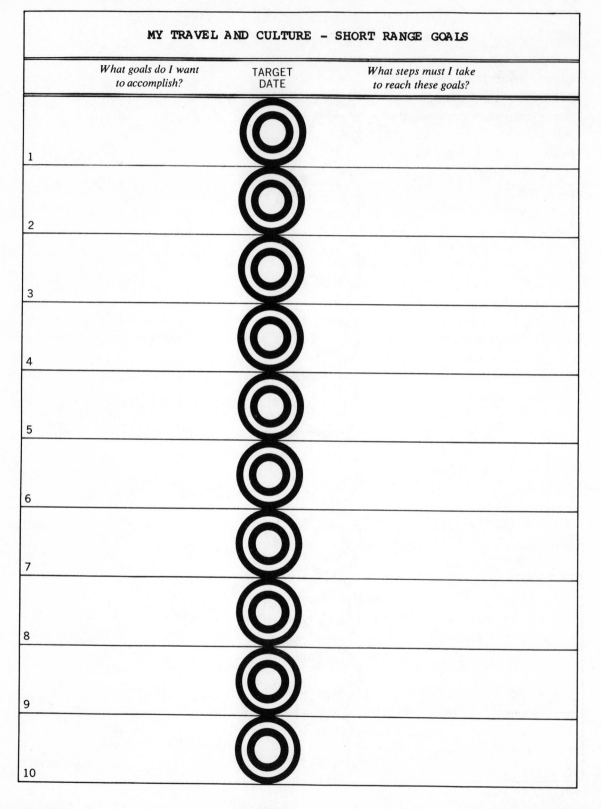

MY TRAVEL AND CULTURE – SHORT RANGE GOALS

	What goals do I want to accomplish?	TARGET DATE	*What steps must I take to reach these goals?*
1			
2			
3			
4			
5			
6			
7			
8			
9			
10			

200

MY TRAVEL AND CULTURE - LONG RANGE GOALS

What goals do I want to accomplish?	TARGET DATE	What steps must I take to reach these goals?
1		
2		
3		
4		
5		
6		
7		
8		
9		
10		

MY PLAN

What do I really want to accomplish? _____
_____
_____
_____
_____
_____

What is the most effective and expedient way of reaching my goal?_____
_____
_____
_____
_____
_____

I have the following abilities, skills, and knowledge for achieving this goal:_____
_____
_____
_____
_____

Additional information, skills, and abilities needed:_____
_____
_____
_____
_____

Here are the places I will go, the people I will see, the sources I will use, to help me gain new knowledge, skills and abilities I need: _____
_____
_____
_____
_____

The first step I will take this week:_____
_____

My next main steps will be as follows (Include deadlines):_____
_____
_____
_____
_____

My target date for reaching this goal: _____

MY SPECIFIC PLAN

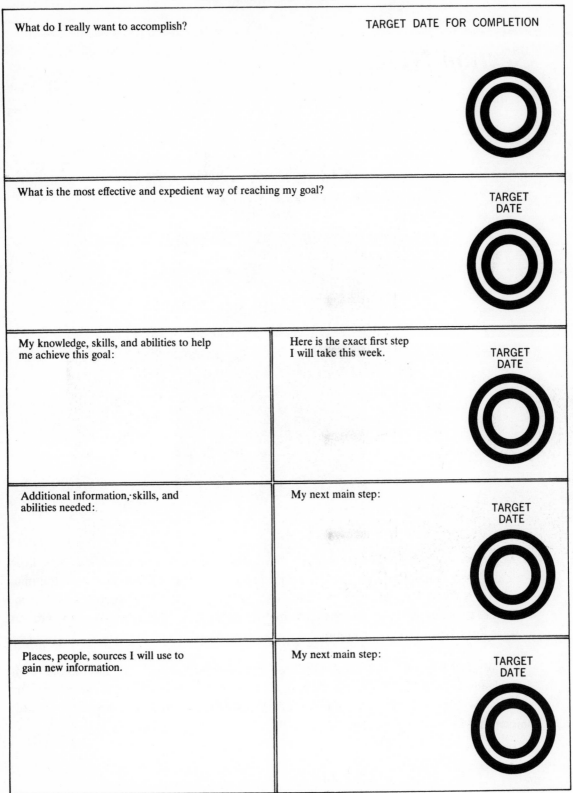

What do I really want to accomplish?

TARGET DATE FOR COMPLETION

What is the most effective and expedient way of reaching my goal?

TARGET
DATE

My knowledge, skills, and abilities to help me achieve this goal:

Here is the exact first step I will take this week.

TARGET
DATE

Additional information, skills, and abilities needed:

My next main step:

TARGET
DATE

Places, people, sources I will use to gain new information.

My next main step:

TARGET
DATE

Section Nine

SOCIAL

Personality

Personal Interests

Environment

Experience

If we reflect on the number of men we have seen and know, and consider how little we have been to them and they to us, what must our feeling be? We meet with the man of genius without conversing with him, with the scholar without learning from him, with the traveller without gaining information from him, the amiable man without making ourselves agreeable to him.

And this alas! happens not merely with passing acquaintances; society and families conduct themselves similarly towards their dearest members, cities towards their worthiest citizens; peoples towards their most excellent princes, and nations towards their most eminent men.

—GOETHE

204

SOCIAL LIFE

Choosing Your Associates

People are the portals through which men pass into positions of power and leadership.

Character is so largely affected by associations that we cannot afford to be indifferent as to who and what our friends are. We should be careful in selecting them for they help make us what we are.

Bad associates have prevented many a person from becoming successful. There are people with whom you can associate and be enriched—others steal your time. Ideally, we should associate with men of judgment for by conversing with them we assimilate their good judgment into our own thoughts and actions. You will find successful businessmen associating with other successful businessmen at their clubs and social gatherings. Environment is more important to a man's success than his heredity.

The Art Of Conversation

A smile is the most becoming thing you can wear. When you speak to people— *smile.* It not only lights up your face, it warms you up inside, helping you to be pleasant and good natured.

Courtesy is found in the large majority of important executives. They are men who, under the most difficult circumstances will listen patiently and maintain a gentlemenly attitude. They know the wheels of business must be lubricated with tact and courtesy or else overheating and friction losses will result.

When you fall into conversation with a person determine first whether he has a greater inclination to hear you, or for you to hear him. Every person has a different background, let them tell you about their business, their interests. You will learn much about the subject that they know the best, and one of the best guides to conversation is to ask questions.

A good point to remember—when dealing with other people we are not dealing with creatures of logic, but rather with creatures of emotion, bustling with prejudices and motivated by pride and vanity.

Rendering A Service

Henry J. Kaiser says: "Love people and serve them." Render a service if you would succeed. This is the supreme law of life. Invest your social hours in productive attainment. You will widen your sphere of influence and meet exceptionally gifted and proficient men who might not otherwise cross your path. Participate in charity groups, service clubs, city and county commissions and boards, chambers of commerce, and the like. It is a great personal satisfaction to know you are doing your part and investing your time.

THE GOLDEN RULES

Be courteous to everyone.
A pleasant smile accomplishes wonders.
Acknowledge all introductions cordially.
Extend a hearty handshake, never a flabby one.
Memorize the names of everyone you meet.
Look people in the eye when conversing.
Talk with calm assurance; do not raise your voice.
Shun idle gossip; never meddle in personal affairs.
Be a good listener; respect others' viewpoints.
Avoid arguments: keep cool, even if provoked.
When you are in the wrong, admit it promptly, frankly.
Be open-minded, tolerant, considerate.
Cooperate readily, cheerfully.
Be a booster! Praise generously! Criticize tactfully.
Show that you appreciate all favors, big or little.
Say "Thank You" expressively, not just politely.
Be sympathetic, but never complain or seek sympathy.
Always be punctual! Keep no one waiting.
Make your work respected by keeping all promises.
Be fair and square, loyal and sincere.
Take pride in your work and appearance.
Do your best—today and every day.
Radiate friendliness, enthusiasm, good will.

Anyone who observes all of these rules would be successful almost automatically, and he would certainly be possessed of many friends.

THOUGHTS ON FRIENDSHIP

To you stranger! If you, passing, meet me, and desire to speak to me, why should you not speak to me? And why should I not speak to you?

—Walt Whitman

How little we know some of our friends, or even some of our relatives. Members of the same family often live in practical isolation; their minds move as if they were in parallel lines and never meet; they are not really in touch with one another.

—John Lubbock

The greatest benefit which one friend can confer upon another is to guard, and excite, and elevate his virtues.

—Samuel Johnson

A real friend is one who will tell you of your faults and follies in prosperity, and assist you with his hand and heart in adversity.

Gold is tried in fire, friendship in need.

—Danish Saying

I desire to conduct the affairs of this administration so that if at the end, when I come to lay down the reins of power, I have lost every other friend on earth, I shall have at least one friend left, and that friend shall be down inside of me.

—Abraham Lincoln

Friendliness: the mysterious cement.

—Charles Gow

Much certainty of the happiness and purity of our lives depends on our making a wise choice of our companions and friends.

—John Lubbock

Reprove thy friend privately, commend him publicly.

—Solon

Every man can tell how many goats or sheep he possesses, but not how many friends.

—Cicero

One thing that I have repeatedly noticed in my experience is that the men who won the very highest honors in business and professional life are almost invariably men with friendly dispositions. Once you obtain an interview with them, they receive you in a cordial manner, indicating that those who have reached high positions have found it necessary to cultivate the attitude of friendliness.

—Charles Gow

Avoid useless arguments. Especially avoid arguments on politics and religion, and controversial subjects. You may win an argument, but lose a friend.

FACES—WHAT THEY SAY

The genteel person has fine-spun hair, fine grained skin, with sharply chisled features. This is a formal person, refined and well-bred. They appreciate music, art, good writing, sports such as golf and tennis.

The person with a high-forehead is courteous. The higher the forehead the more courteous, tactful and polite they are. He is high-minded, agreeable, gracious, pleasant, soft of speech, and kind of manner. He is interested in ideals and principles.

An individual whose face is cube shape or square is a realist. He has broad and powerful shoulders. He sees life as it is, he is constantly observing life. Movement and action are fundamental to his life. He wants to be in the thick of the fight. He is interested in essentials and wants action.

The intellectual type has a V shaped head, small jaw and sharp chin, with a broad and high forehead. He has a thoughtful outlook on life, has high ideals, responds to culture and refinement. His work is done and his battles are won in his mind. He likes accurate brief facts.

Blonde hair, blue or grey eyes, fair, or ruddy, pinkish complexion is an imaginative person. His mind speedily jumps from one thing to another. He is bored with details or hammering on a point, likes conversation that is light and amusing. Redheads are included in this group.

The predominating type person has a head which is wide above the ears. In a group the widest headed person will dominate and persuade the group, he is energetic, he enjoys battling down obstacles.

The individual whose forehead recedes is a rapid thinker. The more slant the faster he thinks. An impatient listener, he likes to see things. Let him do the talking. Answer his questions and negative thoughts immediately.

FACES—WHAT THEY SAY

The speed with which a person acts (not thinks or decides) is indicated by the slant of the chin. A person with a chin that recedes or slants backward acts swiftly, the more slant the more impulsive. Does not tolerate delay, don't keep him waiting. Slanting chin does not indicate weak character.

The brunette with brown or black eyes, and dark complexion is a natural conservative. He absorbs ideas steadily, wants lots of details. He is seldom enthusiastic. Talk to him carefully with solid facts. Don't try to be funny.

A person with a long-upper lip has persistence and tenacity. He is self-willed, capable of sustained practical reasoning. He accepts constructive criticism. He is suspicious of praise and flattery, and resents a flippant attitude. Don't kid him.

Rough skin, rugged heavy features, and stiff course hair are characteristic of a sociable person. He is a good pal, likes exchanging stories, wants things on a familiar basis. Interested in sports, stories of strength, and achievement. He is blunt with broad sense of humor.

The person with a round face, ball-shaped appearance is ease loving. He likes comfort and pleasure. He forms his own opinions about the worth of things. Is shrewd in money matters and wants his money's worth. He wants the good life, and no annoyances.

A protruding chin indicates a person who acts slowly, deliberately. He cannot be rushed, hurried, or pushed into anything. He can be stubborn. In conversation be patient and tactful. Even though he acts deliberately he may be a rapid thinker.

A person with protruding or bulging forehead is a reflective thinker. His thinking is slow, deliberate, reflective. If his forehead bulges out above flat brows he has an innate thirst for knowledge, and desires to accumulate information. Speak slowly and vividly to this person.

LIST OF MY FRIENDS

Be very careful in the selection of your friends.
"The most valuable and fairest furniture of life."

--Cicero

NAME AND ADDRESS	TELEPHONE

MY FIVE BEST FRIENDS:

LIST OF MY FRIENDS

Friends contribute materially toward your education. You derive most
of your knowledge of getting on with people from friends who are sufficiently interested and patient to tell you what they know. It is
only from a friend that you will listen to a disagreeable truth about
yourself. In any way you wish to look at the subject, a friend is an
important asset.
                                                          --Charles Gow

NAME AND ADDRESS	TELEPHONE

One way to keep friends is to remember important dates in their
lives - even in a simple way. Birthday - anniversary - birth
of a child. A note of compliment for some achievement brings a
warm response - heart to heart. A note is better than a phone
call and cards and flowers bring pleasure.

SOCIAL QUESTIONNAIRE

To have friends we must be friendly. There is no treasure greater
than a sincere friend with worthy principles and high purposes. But
if our friends are badly chosen they will inevitably drag us down;
if well chosen they will raise us up. A real friend likes us in
spite of all our faults, and inspires us to be a better person.

It will be noticed that every successful person has a host of
friends, some of whom have helped to make the person a success,
while others have been attracted to him because of his success.

Are you a friendly person?_____

How many really close friends do you have?_____

Do you have one or two good friends whom you can depend on?_____
_____Can they depend on you?_____

Do you choose people with whom you just spend your time, or people
with whom you invest your time?_____

Are you always planning, striving for the best things in life?_____

Do you keep your promises? Are you prompt for appointments?_____

Are you curious about other peoples lives? Do you ask too many
questions? Do you gossip about your boss, or your fellow workers?

Do you distinguish between the different qualities of friends or
acquaintances and give them time and attention accordingly?_____

Do you have a regular schedule for doing things for your friends
and relatives? (Remember birthdays, anniversaries, call or write
regularly, give them gifts, do special things for them, help them
achieve their desires)?_____

What improvements would you like to make in your personality to
make yourself more appealing to others?_____

Just how important are friends to you? Write out your philosophy
of friendship_____

212

SUGGESTED GOALS AND OBJECTIVES
For My Social Life

Plan and do things for my friends and relatives.

Develop my personality, poise, and manners.

Smile, be genuinely friendly all the time.

Take a genuine interest in other people.

Acquire new friends.

Do things to make others happy.

Improve my conversation, become a better listener.

Take a course in public speaking.

Join a club or group to make new friends, and develop my social skills, such as a church, service, fraternal, political, civic, or business group.

Plan my wardrobe and dress properly for all occasions.

Plan social gatherings with a purpose.

Learn to handle people tactfully.

Develop self-control and discard bad habits of temper, impatience, touchiness, egotism, selfishness.

If single—spend more time doing things for others.

Work at making my home life happy and enjoyable.

Discard negative friends and acquaintances.

Ships that pass in the night, and speak to each other in passing. Only a signal shown, and a distant voice in the darkness; So on the ocean of life we pass and speak one to another, only a look and a voice; then darkness again and a silence.

—Longfellow

SOCIAL RULES

Etiquette is the science of living.

Praise people when they do a good job.

Don't criticize, it lowers the morale of any group.

Shun gossip. The person who gossips to you will gossip about you.

Do not argue. Why win an argument and lose a friend.

Give the new member or employee a cheerful welcome.

Encourage people. Encouragement is oxygen to the soul.

Politics can be poison, never let yourself be drawn into talking politics with a customer.

Keep your personal appearance neat and clean.

Courtesy is the lubricant of friendship.

Put yourself occasionally in the other fellow's shoes, try to see his point of view.

Be polite—remember the value of saying "Thank You."

Good manners are the enjoyable way of doing things.

To keep friends you have to carry your half of the friendship.

We must be honest and admit that there are certain people who you should stay away from. Once you know them to be negative, crooked, destructive, harmful—for your own good—stay away from them. Keep out of the suction caused by those who are drifting backward.

MY SOCIAL LIFE – SHORT RANGE GOALS

What goals do I want to accomplish?	TARGET DATE	What steps must I take to reach these goals?
1		
2		
3		
4		
5		
6		
7		
8		
9		
10		

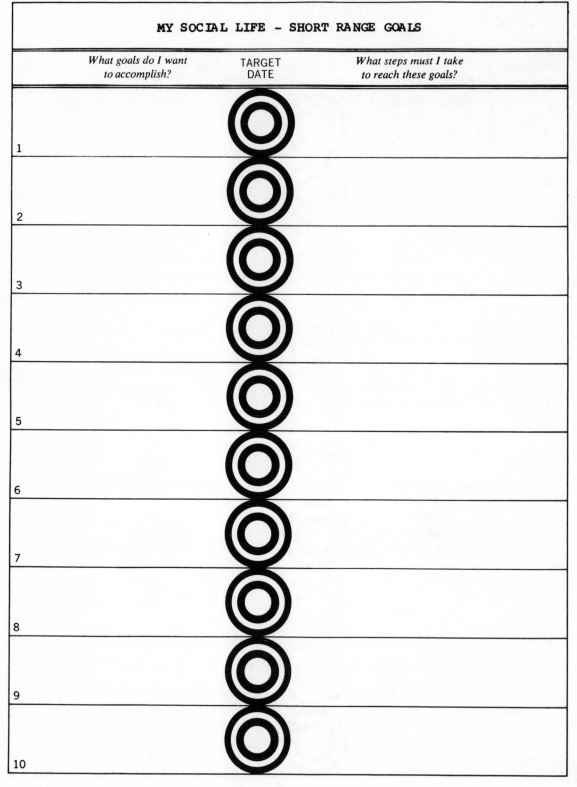

214

MY SOCIAL LIFE - LONG RANGE GOALS		
What goals do I want to accomplish?	TARGET DATE	*What steps must I take to reach these goals?*
1		
2		
3		
4		
5		
6		
7		
8		
9		
10		

MY PLAN

What do I really want to accomplish? _____

_____

_____

_____

_____

_____

What is the most effective and expedient way of reaching my goal? _____

_____

_____

_____

_____

_____

I have the following abilities, skills, and knowledge for achieving this goal: _____

_____

_____

_____

_____

Additional information, skills, and abilities needed: _____

_____

_____

_____

_____

Here are the places I will go, the people I will see, the sources I will use, to help me gain new knowledge, skills and abilities I need: _____

_____

_____

_____

_____

_____

The first step I will take this week: _____

_____

_____

My next main steps will be as follows (Include deadlines): _____

_____

_____

_____

_____

_____

My target date for reaching this goal: _____

216

MY SPECIFIC PLAN

What do I really want to accomplish?

TARGET DATE FOR COMPLETION

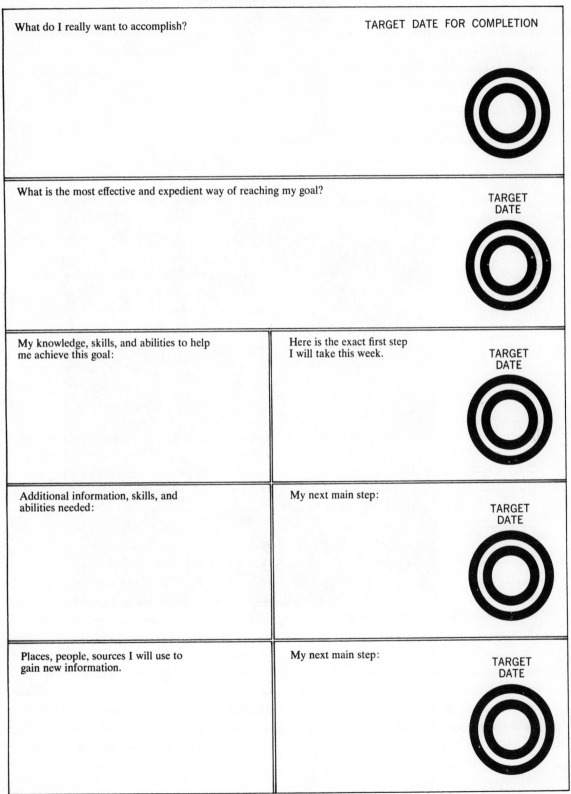

What is the most effective and expedient way of reaching my goal?

TARGET DATE

My knowledge, skills, and abilities to help me achieve this goal:

Here is the exact first step I will take this week.

TARGET DATE

Additional information, skills, and abilities needed:

My next main step:

TARGET DATE

Places, people, sources I will use to gain new information.

My next main step:

TARGET DATE

Section Ten

SPIRITUAL

Spiritual power is a force which history clearly teaches has been the greatest force in the development of man. Yet we have been merely playing with it and never really studied it as we have the physical forces. Some day people will learn that material things do not bring happiness, and are of little use in making people creative and powerful. Then the scientists of the world will turn their laboratories over to the study of spiritual forces which have hardly been scratched.

—CHARLES STEINMETZ

218

SPIRITUAL LIFE

In this present age of complexities where careful planning is so important, the author deigns to make a minor change in the homespun saying "cleanliness is godliness" by saying that "orderliness is godliness."

All about us we are constantly reminded of a great power that has set up inexorable laws by which we must abide for our safety, health and well-being. Although we take it all for granted we do have the assurance that the sun will rise each morning and set each evening, and we are able to calculate in advance, for years to come, the exact movement of each.

We can depend upon the tides and the seasons. The day, the month, the year, and even the tenth part of the minute used by the industrial engineer, or the fractional part of a second used by the physicist are all the result of man's confidence in the absolute orderliness of the Creator.

We are a part of a great unchanging system of orderliness and of a universe controlled by a Supreme Power we call God, and it behooves us to practice the orderliness which is Godliness. Even the most cynical must admit that conformity to the laws of God in the universe have their own rewards.

The power which has established and maintains this orderliness in the universe is available to us to guide and empower our lives if we will draw upon it. God is not merely a Creator of a universe who has set the world spinning and left it to go its merry way. His infinite care is demonstrated in the cause, and effect, action and reaction pattern built into the universe. Everything is made to perpetuate itself. There is available to every living thing the resources within its environment that it needs to sustain its life.

Modern man demands to know the how of all he accepts. There is no scientist who can explain the mystery of physical birth, the mystery of the electron, the bewildering phenomenon of germination, or the baffling riddle of a lily's growth. Who can explain with reason and logic why a caterpillar goes into his cocoon and later comes out a beautiful butterfly?

Every creature known to science, except man, is perfectly built for adjustment to the present physical environment of our world. It would not tax the genius of a scientist at all to definitely establish the fact that a fish is built for water. His gills, fins and entire make-up prove conclusively that water is his environment. Just so, the wings and general make-up of a bird argues that it was built for air. By exactly the same method of study, man reveals himself to have been created by God for fellowship with God.

This world was made for man. Man is God's agent here on earth. There is a supreme power outside of man and a power within every man. It is up to each of us to recognize this power and use it if we would live the way we are designed to live.

In one form or another, as far back as it is possible to trace human history, man's deepest concern has ever been to reach things beyond the ken of his intellect. The savage at his crude altar, the Aborigine sacrificing to his gods of wood and stone, the fire worshipper turning his face to the rising sun, and modern man with his multiple religions, creeds, doctrines, dogmas and philosophies all testify to the fact that man can no more escape the call of the Eternal than he can escape the fact of his own being.

Man is basically a spiritual being—his equipment for living far surpasses any visible resources available in his environment. His spirit calls out for a greater destiny. It demands a greater satisfaction than is ever possible within the confines of the visible universe. This longing is spiritual. And God has provided man with the resources he needs in the spiritual realm to satisfy the longings of his heart and to fulfill his destiny to a far greater extent than we would dream.

The key to this power is the *USE* of it. And it is available to every individual. When we round out our life to include a well developed spiritual awareness we become a powerful, resolute individual who is capable of meeting life's problems, capable of reaching our highest desires for our own lives, and contributing to the higher attainment of others. We are capable of deep abiding love, devotion to our family, loyalty to our jobs, courage in times of danger, strength in times of temptation, power in times of trial.

Use the questionnaire on the following pages to help you analyze your own spiritual philosophy, where you are right now, and what improvements you would like to make. It may be the most important planning action you could take in your life. By now your Manual is probably full of wonderful and exciting plans and ideas for your future. The greatest insurance policy you can have for their completion, and your ability to accomplish them, is the deepening of your spiritual life.

If our accomplishments in the world are meted out to us "according to our faith," how vital it is to enlarge our faith now—so the rest of our life can be more meaningful. Truly, you will find when the spiritual has its rightful place in your life, that every day is a new and glorious experience, charged with meaning and purpose. When we know where we are going, and feel capable of getting there, we can do anything that is within our capacity. It is God's power abiding in us that gives us this confidence and help.

MY CHURCH ACTIVITIES

Church going is important to our lives because it provides that needed change of pace for our bodies, minds, spirits. Here those who are weary of the burden of daily cares should find a moment's meditation in the contemplation of the higher life.
To raise society to a higher level and to overcome evil with good is the genius of Christianity.

--A. A. M.

Church Memberships: (Name of church, location, dates belonged, minister's name, etc.)

_____
_____
_____
_____
_____

Baptisms, confirmations of our family: (Persons name, church, (officiating minister, dates, where are records kept?)

_____
_____
_____
_____

Church Activities I Have Participated In:

Attended Sunday School, or Study Group_____

Class officer, group leader_____
Taught Sunday School_____Age Group_____Years_____
Sang in Choir_____
Usher_____Board Member_____
Church Officer_____
Special projects (fund raising, building improvement, chaperone,etc):
_____
_____

Outstanding preachers, teachers I have heard speak:_____
_____

Studies I have completed (Bible studies, communicants classes, etc.):
_____

Family Participation - Activities of my wife and children:_____
_____

Activities I would like to be a part of: New skills I have acquired through church participation: special areas where I can contribute to the church:_____
_____
_____

ESSENTIAL KNOWLEDGE

We have been told that the realm of knowledge is so vast that to touch more than the fringe of it during a lifetime of study is quite impossible. In one sense, that is true. In another sense, it is quite untrue. If, by knowledge, one means all that pertains to life, the universe and to the earth on which we live, then, of course, a lifetime is not long enough to investigate such unthinkable realms. If, by knowledge, one means essential information concerning such facts as have to do with fulfilling the prime objective of the Creator, then a lifetime, be it short or long, provides more than sufficient time to acquire such essential knowledge.

Christianity opens to us a whole realm of essential knowledge, and it is a means of acquiring essential knowledge. Why do I use that word essential? Because after all, much that we call knowledge is not, in the last analysis, essential knowledge. Essential knowledge then, is the knowledge that gives point and meaning to life itself. Essential knowledge is "indispensable truth that I must know."

The Bible is God's revelation to man. It meets all the tests, provides all the needed truth and points to the highest life known. This revelation is at once the vindication of a God who is infinite in wisdom and mercy, and who has made full provision for man whose limited knowledge demands such a revelation.

The Bible deals with eternal values and is a source of help with the mundane things we have to deal with every day. We need the Bible to guide us in our every day living. The Bible is the Word of God and is the best guide to life. It gives us confidence, hope, peace of mind, inspiration in our everyday living. That is one of the many reasons I say, "to know God is to be adjusted to daily living." To know is—to experience God— to fellowship with God—to enjoy God—to appreciate God. No man will live the way he is designed to live without having God in his heart, and nothing will satisfy a man that is lasting and permanent except having God in his heart.

But how to "know God?" . . . The only way to "know God" is to experience Him, to fellowship, to appreciate, to enjoy Him. Physical birth is for a physical world, but there is a realm above the physical. To enter that realm "ye must be born again from above . . . by the Spirit." Such a birth is essential knowledge.

God in you is the hope of Glory. To live gloriously, is to live normally. To live normally is to function in the purpose for which we were created, namely: Fellowship with God. This is made possible only by His "indwelling presence."

SPIRITUAL QUOTATIONS

Human nature being as it is, the average person's thoughts turn to God only when he is in some trouble, seriously ill, financially despondent, suffering the loss of a loved one, lost in the mountains, buckling on a life preserver, or worshipping in a church service.

—A. A. M.

Just as a candle cannot burn without a fire, men cannot live without a spiritual life. The spirit dwells in all men, but not all men are aware of this. Happy is the life of him who knows this, and unhappy his life who does not know it.

—Buddha

You are made for God, just like your eye is made for light. You cannot see in the dark. You cannot find peace except in the will of God for "thy will is my peace."
With all the sincerity of my eighty years, I say, God is the answer to the modern confusion that dogs us.

—Frank Buchman

Prayer is a force as real as terrestrial gravity. As a physician, I have seen men, after all other therapy had failed, lifted out of disease and melancholy by the serene effort of prayer. Only in prayer do we achieve that complete and harmonious assembly of body, mind and spirit which gives the frail human reed its unshakable strength.

—Alexis Carrel

Observation and experience has taught me that every man must go through the fire. This means that during your lifetime you will experience great suffering or great sorrow, and you will need the help of God to win over your problems.

—A. A. M.

The Bible tells us how to secure the good things—"Seek ye first the Kingdom of God, and his righteousness; and all these things shall be added unto you." Can we live according to God's plan for us? Can we place our love for God and our fellowmen first in our hearts? If we can, then good things are in store for us.

—Grenville Kleiser

Man's true aim is to glorify God and enjoy Him forever.

—Westminster Catechism

The mistake of men is, and ever has been, to think of the physical man as the real man and the physical world as the real world. The real man, the scriptures insist, is the spiritual man, and the real world is the spiritual. The real man does not, because he cannot, live on stocks and bonds, houses and lands, mortgages and commodities. By every scientific test he is built for God and spiritual things. With God he must have fellowship or be in this, and every other world, a bewildered, unhappy, discontented creature. It is not *WHERE* we are or *WHAT* we have that makes us happy or unhappy. No generation ever had so much; no generation has so little. We must find God or lose everything.

—A. P. Gouthey

Happy is the man who has learned the secret of coming to God daily in prayer. Fifteen minutes alone with God every morning before you start the day can change circumstances and remove mountains.

—Billy Graham

God is at the center of man.

—Eckhart

All purely human ideas of God are necessarily imperfect. Our ideas are qualified and limited by what we have seen and known. He is the way of life that we were created to live. With Him life has meaning; without Him men exist in a meaningless discord.

—A. P. Gouthey

Modern society has committed the fundamental error of disobeying the law of spiritual development. It has arbitrarily reduced spirit to mere intellect. It has cultivated the intellect because, thanks to science, the intellect gives it mastery of the physical world, but has ignored those other activities of the spirit which can never be more than partially represented in scientific language and which are only expressed in action, art and prayer.

—Alexis Carrel

There is a critical age, around fifty, in spiritual life, when a man begins to think seriously about life and to make up his mind on its meaning. Generally the decision he then comes to is irrevocable. What a misfortune if it is wrong.

—Leo Tolstoy

What we are within registers itself without. A river first digs a channel, then the channel controls the river. Men do not deliberately set out to become villains, drunks, thieves, and rakes. They gradually become all these things by allowing themselves to become victims of the stream that cuts the channel of living deeper and deeper. By the same token, the soul becomes subordinated to high moral and spiritual faculties until at last such spiritual faculties become the dominating power in life. Thus, and only thus, can any of us come to his highest and best and fullest living.

—A. P. Gouthey

There are three ways that prepare us for life's trials. One is the Spartan way that says, "I have strength within me to do it, I am the captain of my soul. With the courage and will that is mine, I will be master when the struggle comes." Another way is in the spirit of Socrates, who affirmed that we have minds, reason, and judgment to evaluate and help us to cope with the enigmas and struggles of life. The Christian way is the third approach. It doesn't exclude the first two, but it adds, "You don't begin with yourself, your will or your reason. Faith in the Creator gives you the power to overcome all things."

—Lowell R. Ditzen

SPIRITUAL QUESTIONNAIRE

It is a natural instinct born in man to have the desire for spiritual development. Man's soul needs spiritual food just like his
body needs food, water and air. In the human species, spiritual
development is the Supreme Law.

By our very nature we are spiritual beings. We all know that true
peace of mind comes from God. How many times in our lives we have
looked to Him for help, strength, and guidance, never to be denied.

Spiritual wealth makes a man richer than all the gold of Crocsus.
                                           --Roger Babson

Do you have a true sense of the spiritual? Are you satisfied with
the extent of your present spiritual life?_____
_____
_____

Do you have faith in God?_____

Does the quality of your spiritual life help you meet the everyday
problems in a confident manner?_____

Do you have peace of mind to the extent that you feel comfortable
in the world and ready to meet anything that comes along?_____
_____
_____

Do you have a personal acquaintance with God where you feel his
indwelling presence and direction in your life?_____
_____
_____

What progress would you like to make along these lines?_____
_____
_____

Am I using the power that is available to me through God's guidance in my life, or have I been neglecting this source of power?
Do I need to improve my spiritual life so I will have more power
to meet daily living? _____
_____
_____
_____

How will I strengthen my spiritual life? By inspirational reading,
prayer, meditation, Bible study, church attendance, other?_____
_____
_____
_____
_____
_____

SPIRITUAL QUESTIONNAIRE

Am I satisfied with the meaning of life that I now have? Do I
want to expand my grasp of the meaning and purpose of life? What
can I do to enlarge my understanding? _____
_____
_____
_____
_____

Am I afraid to die? Why? Do I need my faith strengthened? Do I
need more purpose for living, more accomplishment so that if I
die prematurely, I will have left something worthy behind me?____
_____
_____
_____
_____

Is my family close together through spiritual understanding? Can
this be improved? In what way?_____
_____
_____
_____

Do I give strength and encouragement to those around me?_____

Am I a tower of strength - resolute, trusting, drawing upon God's
power? Do I use the knowledge and resources that are available
to me in the universe; in my immediate surroundings; within my
own being - my talents, abilities, character? What would I like
to improve? How can I get started?_____
_____
_____
_____
_____
_____
_____

SUGGESTED GOALS AND OBJECTIVES

Personal meditation and prayer.
Consistent Bible reading and study.
Greater personal faith and trust.
More understanding of spiritual things.
Meditate about the meaning of my life.
Formulate my spiritual philosophy, and ethical standards.
Attend church regularly, participate in church activities.
Read inspirational, spiritual books and magazines.
Seek guidance from those spiritual persons I respect.
More family participation in Bible reading,prayer, and discussion.
Plan a program for spiritual growth.

226

GOALS FOR MY SPIRITUAL LIFE

	What goals do I want to accomplish?	TARGET DATE	*What steps must I take to reach these goals?*
1			
2			
3			
4			
5			
6			
7			
8			
9			
10			

MY PLAN

What do I really want to accomplish? _____

_____

_____

_____

_____

_____

What is the most effective and expedient way of reaching my goal? _____

_____

_____

_____

_____

I have the following abilities, skills, and knowledge for achieving this goal: ___

_____

_____

_____

_____

Additional information, skills, and abilities needed: _____

_____

_____

_____

_____

Here are the places I will go, the people I will see, the sources I will use, to help me gain new knowledge, skills and abilities I need: _____

_____

_____

_____

_____

_____

The first step I will take this week: _____

_____

My next main steps will be as follows (Include deadlines): _____

_____

_____

_____

_____

My target date for reaching this goal: _____

228

MY SPECIFIC PLAN

What do I really want to accomplish?

TARGET DATE FOR COMPLETION

What is the most effective and expedient way of reaching my goal?

TARGET
DATE

My knowledge, skills, and abilities to help me achieve this goal:	Here is the exact first step I will take this week. TARGET DATE
Additional information, skills, and abilities needed:	My next main step: TARGET DATE
Places, people, sources I will use to gain new information.	My next main step: TARGET DATE

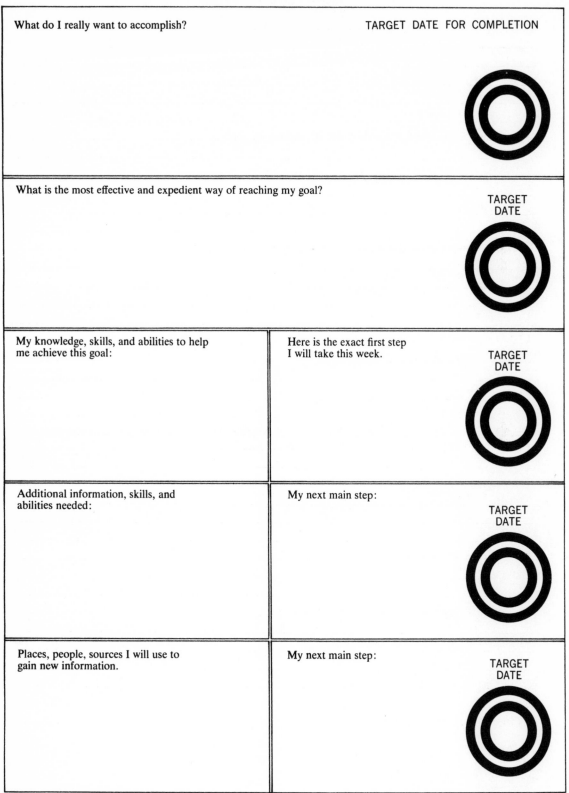

RETIREMENT and WILL

"ALL THIS SHALL PASS AWAY."   Then why not enjoy the few days we have on our earthly home? All we have is just loaned to us. When a man has accumulated enough of the material goods to live comfortably on, why does he keep loading himself up with more and more, instead of enjoying what he has? Greed for wealth in old age is foolish; for what can be more absurd than to increase our provisions for the road ahead the nearer we approach to our journey's end?

YOUR RETIREMENT YEARS

Think about your retirement—not when you approach age 65 but today.

What happens to you at age 65 depends entirely on your planning and how you order your life today. Many older folks now in retirement, as well as many experts in the field, say emphatically that it's never too early to begin thinking and planning for one's retirement.

In retirement, you are no longer a servant to the alarm clock; there are no deadlines to meet; the commuter traffic is not your worry. You can be just as productive or as lazy as you choose. And how many people have you heard say "I can't wait until I retire. Then I can do what I always wanted to do." Yes, these can be your most fruitful years.

WHAT ABOUT MY HEALTH?

Retirement planning can be divided into four areas: Health, finance, home, and "you." The order is important because without good health your financial resources, your outlook on life itself will suffer correspondingly.

Regular check-ups are a start, but you must not rely on a hoped-for clean bill of health. Without a sensible approach to your daily living, you will be trusting your future happiness to pure luck. Try to keep your weight down and your exercise up. Live within your own physical means; temper your activities to fit your years. And, of course, be acutely aware of the body's danger signals such as fatigue, shortness of breath, pain or stiffness of limbs. Follow closely your doctor's recommendations and good health will be more than chance.

WILL I HAVE ENOUGH MONEY TO LIVE ON?

Money is always a problem. Why not draw up a projected budget? List your estimated income from the company's pension plan, your Social Security benefits, insurance policies that may reach maturity and any other assets that will supplement your retirement wage. Now put down a retirement budget. (Use pages 233–235.)

It is reasonable to assume that you will cut down on certain expenses, but before you arrive at a figure, be certain that you are economizing wisely. An item such as a telephone will be as important to you in your retirement as it is today. And if you plan to work, even if it is only part time, remember, that working costs money in travel, lunch, clothes and cleaning bills. Also consider what bearing this extra income will have on your pension and income tax; know the "work clause" provisions of Social Security which presently allows you to earn $125 per month. All over that amount reduces your social security income.

Make sure that you set down all your fixed liabilities; health insurance payments, continuing life insurance policies, all automobile expenses, even a leverage factor for real estate taxes that are sure to rise. What is your present indebtedness. Is it a long range problem? A loan, mortgage, or even time payments carried into retirement can prove disastrous to your budget.

Put plenty of careful thought into every figure that becomes a part of your final estimate, for these numbers represent your future. Will you have enough money to be happy and live comfortably? If not, you had better find ways of adding to the asset side of the ledger. Talk to your attorney, banker and life insurance agent, when considering your financial program. There are any number of ways that you can help yourself now, but maybe not, later. Prepare yourself now for life on a lower income.

WHERE SHALL I LIVE?

There is another factor that pertains to both finance and "you." Perhaps the easiest item in your budget to trim is your home. You can even make some money on it if you are fortunate. No longer are you forced to live within a reasonable commuting distance. Maybe the house is too big, anyway. Couldn't you move to a smaller place or an apartment where upkeep, maintenance and over-all costs would be far less?

If you do decide to move investigate your move thoroughly ahead of time—even if it is within the same town. Are you leaving family behind? Will you like a different climate? Make sure there are adequate and convenient shopping, hospital, and medical facilities nearby. The best solution is to give your prospective location a fair trial. Go there on your vacations and practice living within your retirement income. Unless you are positive, don't buy. Rent for six months or a year; give yourself a chance to gain the right perspective.

WHAT WILL I DO?

The fourth phase is "you" . . . the psychological aspect of retirement. This is the little voice that says, "Oh, sure I move a little slower, but I'm just as sharp as I ever was. With my experience and zest for life there are any number of things that I can do, contributions that I can make."

What do you enjoy doing—building with your hands, the outdoors, writing, working with people? Now is the time to involve yourself in activities that correspond with your interests. A simple hobby today may be your life work in retirement. Start taking an interest in community work, recreation, etc. This would not only allow you a source of continued contribution, but would maintain that familiar interplay of people working together that you had on your job.

No one can successfully retire without financial security.

232

PLANNING FOR THE LATER YEARS

I plan to retire from business, but not from life, when I reach _____years of age.

My total monthly income will be: $ _____
(See pgs. 234-235 for details).

My total monthly expenses will be: $ _____
(See pgs. 234-235 for details).

I will have $_____in reserve for emergencies.

Where shall I live? (Name the state, city and location)._____
_____
_____
_____

Will I have enough money to live on?_____
_____
_____
_____

What will I do?_____
_____
_____
_____

What about my health?_____
_____
_____
_____

What are my plans?_____
_____
_____
_____

Are plans for the continuation of my business in order?_____
_____

Do I have a sound, up-to-date will drawn by an attorney?_____
_____

If I do have a will, is it regularly reviewed and revised with births, marriages, deaths?_____

Is the will coordinated with that of my wife (or husband)?_____
_____

Have I provided an experienced executor with investment and dis-cretionary powers broad enough to protect my family?_____
_____

YOUR RETIREMENT BALANCE SHEET

WHAT I OWN

	Now	When I Retire
Home...........................	$ _____	$ _____
Furniture......................	_____	_____
Savings accounts...............	_____	_____
Government bonds................	_____	_____
Stocks.........................	_____	_____
Automobile.....................	_____	_____
Rental property................	_____	_____
Personal property..............	_____	_____
Other..........................	_____	_____
Total that I own........	$ _____	$ _____

WHAT I OWE

	Now	When I Retire
Mortgage on house..............	$ _____	_____
Amount due on car..............	_____	_____
Amount due on furniture........	_____	_____
Amount due on appliances.......	_____	_____
Loans..........................	_____	_____
Other..........................	_____	_____
_____	_____	_____
_____	_____	_____
Total that I owe........	$ _____	$ _____

INSURANCE PROTECTION FOR MY FAMILY

	Now	When I Retire
Life Insurance.................	$ _____	$ _____
Accident insurance.............	_____	_____
Health insurance...............	_____	_____
Personal insurance policies with:.	_____	_____
_____	_____	_____
_____	_____	_____
_____	_____	_____
_____	_____	_____
Total Insurance........	$ _____	_____

ESTIMATE OF MONTHLY INCOME AND EXPENSES

INCOME

	Now	After I Retire
Pension............................	$_____	$_____
Social Security Benefits:		
Mine............................	_____	_____
Spouse..........................	_____	_____
From my savings:		
Interest on savings accounts...	_____	_____
Interest on bonds..............	_____	_____
Dividends on stock.............	_____	_____
Other Income:		
Profit from my business........	_____	_____
Real estate rentals............	_____	_____
Income from another job........	_____	_____
Any other source...............	_____	_____
_____..............		
My total monthly income	$_____	$_____

EXPENSES

	Now	After I Retire
Rent or mortgage..................	$_____	$_____
Food..............................	_____	_____
Clothing..........................	_____	_____
Amusement.........................	_____	_____
Doctor,dentist bills,hospitals....	_____	_____
Automobile expense................	_____	_____
Gas, electricity,telephone,etc....	_____	_____
House repairs and maintenance.....	_____	_____
Furniture.........................	_____	_____
Working expenses (lunch,auto,etc).	_____	_____
Personal items....................	_____	_____
Life insurance....................	_____	_____
Other insurance...................	_____	_____
Income taxes......................	_____	_____
Other taxes.......................	_____	_____
Retirement deductions.............	_____	_____
Health benefit premiums...........	_____	_____
Other items.......................	_____	_____
My total monthly expenses	$_____	$_____

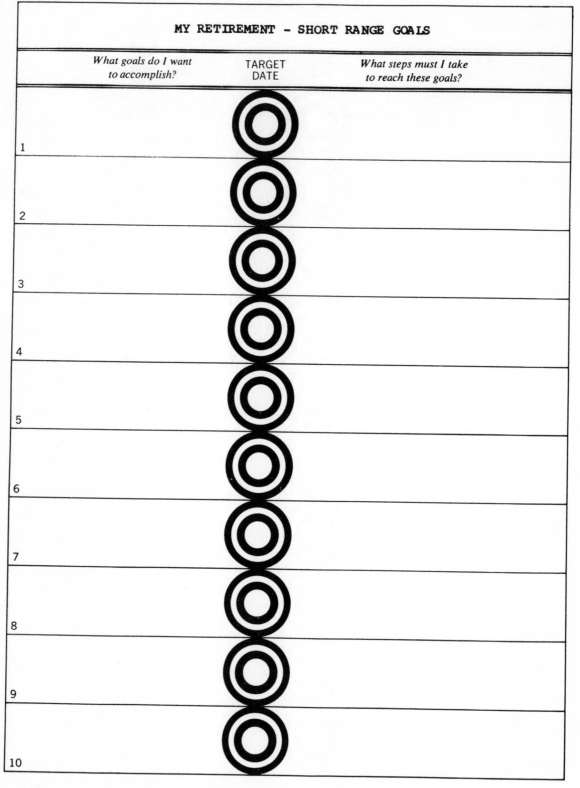

	MY RETIREMENT – SHORT RANGE GOALS		
	What goals do I want to accomplish?	TARGET DATE	*What steps must I take to reach these goals?*
1			
2			
3			
4			
5			
6			
7			
8			
9			
10			

236

MY RETIREMENT - LONG RANGE GOALS

What goals do I want to accomplish?	TARGET DATE	What steps must I take to reach these goals?
1		
2		
3		
4		
5		
6		
7		
8		
9		
10		

MY PLAN

What do I really want to accomplish? _____
_____
_____
_____
_____
_____

What is the most effective and expedient way of reaching my goal? _____
_____
_____
_____
_____
_____

I have the following abilities, skills, and knowledge for achieving this goal: _____
_____
_____
_____
_____

Additional information, skills, and abilities needed: _____
_____
_____
_____
_____

Here are the places I will go, the people I will see, the sources I will use, to help me gain new knowledge, skills and abilities I need: _____
_____
_____
_____
_____
_____

The first step I will take this week: _____
_____

My next main steps will be as follows (Include deadlines): _____
_____
_____
_____
_____
_____

My target date for reaching this goal: _____

MY SPECIFIC PLAN

What do I really want to accomplish?

TARGET DATE FOR COMPLETION

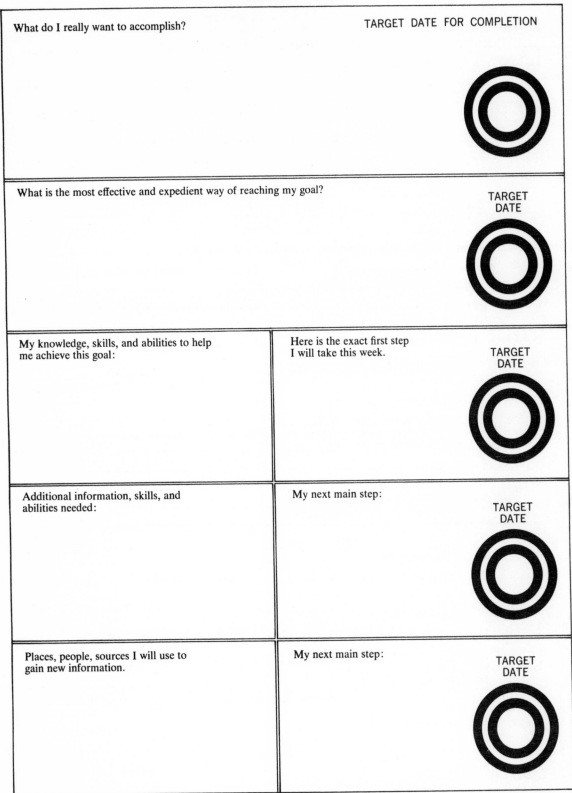

What is the most effective and expedient way of reaching my goal?

TARGET
DATE

My knowledge, skills, and abilities to help me achieve this goal:

Here is the exact first step I will take this week.

TARGET
DATE

Additional information, skills, and abilities needed:

My next main step:

TARGET
DATE

Places, people, sources I will use to gain new information.

My next main step:

TARGET
DATE

FACING REALITY CHECKLIST

The Just In Case Facts

1. Husband's will was last brought up to date on_____.

2. The will is now located at_____.

3. _____has a copy of the will.

4. If husband should die, the family would have a monthly income of:

   $_____ From social security (survivors).

   $_____ From life insurance.

   $_____ From investments.

   $_____ From trusts.

   $_____ From other.

5. In event of above, family should (check which one)

   Sell home and move to less expensive quarters ( )
   Keep home and maintain it   ( )

6. In event of above, wife should seek business advice and help from:_____.

7. The following friends and relatives owe us money:

Name	Amount	Comments
_____	$_____	_____
_____	$_____	_____
_____	$_____	_____

8. We owe money to the following friends and relatives:

	Amount	Comments
_____	$_____	_____
_____	$_____	_____
_____	$_____	_____

Major Financial Hurdles To Be Cleared

1. By the year_____we will need about $_____for college costs.

2. By the year_____we will need about $_____ for travel.

3. By the year_____we will need about $_____To meet the following obligation _____

4. Because of the above, we should be putting away each month...
   $_____.

240

MY WILL

Over a period of time, good money management or good business fortune, or both, may cause your net worth to grow to a substantial figure. With the face amounts of your insurance added, you may have a sizable estate. To make sure that this estate reaches the hands you intend, in the way you intend, at the time you intend, you need the help of an attorney in drawing up a will.

Too many executives fritter away the fruits of a lifetime's work by failure to plan their estates properly. The law may then impose arbitrary or costly provisions. Taxes cut into assets severely, there isn't enough cash when it's needed—and family security is lost. Estate planning is a projection of your family's future, and can mean substantial savings.

Both you and your wife should make wills which agree on how to divide your estate. It should also name a guardian for your minor children in case you both die together.

For your executor—the person to be authorized by the court to supervise the distribution of your estate—choose someone whose intelligence, sanity, and honesty you trust, and who is likely to outlive you. Get this person's agreement to serve as your executor.

Specify that your executor can serve without a bond. This will avoid a bonding charge against your estate. Sign only one copy of your will. The court recognizes only one "original."

Sign your will before at least the minimum number of witnesses required by your state who are not beneficiaries. The more the better. They should be people who later can be reached easily to confirm your signature.

Keep the original signed copy in a secure place where it will be readily found (an unsigned copy will probably stay in the lawyer's files). Your safe-deposit box is a good place for the original, or preferably your home safe if you have one. In most states the safe deposit boxes are sealed by the court on their owner's deaths, but courts will usually authorize any interested party such as your executor, to open the box to get the will.

Tell your lawyer, your executor, and your spouse where the will is kept. Also, keep a note of its whereabouts with your personal papers at home, and record it in this Planning Manual.

Review your will periodically to make sure it still reflects your wishes. You may want to change it if family conditions change such as one of your beneficiaries dies, a child marries, or your tax bracket changes so much that you want to minimize inheritance taxes.

INFLUENCE

The influence of a man's life lives on whether he is alive or dead, whether it is good or evil. We are all responsible for our influence. The influence of great men will live on through the centuries.

THE LAST TIME

Some day you will use your tools for the last time. You will put away your tools and close your tool box. 999 chances out of a thousand you will not know it is for the last time. Some day you will say your last prayer, you may not know it is the last time. You may be like the soldier fatally wounded who started his prayer, but never finished it. I stood for a long time in the doorway of my office, reluctant to leave it, for the last time.

TOO OLD TO BE USEFUL?

Don't you believe it! It is the author's contention that all corporations should have a group of capable experienced men whom they can call on for guidance.

Frank Pace of General Dynamics said: "My job is to weld thinkers and doers." The unbeatable combination is youth for the foot work and experience for the head work. "Old men for counsel, young men for action." Capable men with years of experience are the gyroscopes of any organization. Strange but true is the fact that a man does his best work after fifty years of age.

Only years make men. Rarely do the great men of history distinguish themselves before they are fifty; and between fifty and eighty they do their best work—both as regards quality and quantity.

Voltaire, the French poet and philosopher, did his best work after fifty, and at eighty-four, just before his death, was still producing great writings.

Gladstone, that grand old English statesman, was a potent figure in the political and educational life of Great Britain when he was eighty years of age.

Goethe, no doubt the greatest modern poet of Germany, wrote the first part of "Faust" when fifty-six, and the second part when he was eighty-two.

Jules Verne, author, gave to the world some of his best stories when past seventy.

Noah Webster, when between sixty and seventy, performed the Herculean task of his life in the production of his dictionary.

Bacon, whose works are widely read and universally admired, was sixty years of age before he arrived at the full maturity of his genius.

Socrates, a leader of Greek thought and culture, gave to the world his wisest sayings at the age of sixty-eight.

Victor Hugo, foremost man of letters of his time, wrote "Les Miserables" when sixty years of age.

Ralph Waldo Emerson, American essayist, poet, and philosopher, wrote his "Conduct of Life" at fifty-seven.

Michelangelo painted the ceiling of the Sistine Chapel (on his back, on a scaffold) when he was nearly ninety.

And this list can go on and on . . .

IN MEMORIAM

But oh, for the touch of a vanished hand
And the sound of a voice that is still.

                              --Tennyson

Name	Passed Away Mo. Day Yr.	Place of Memorial Service

WAITING

Serene I fold my hands and wait,
Nor care for wind, nor tide, nor sea,
I rave no more 'gainst time or fate,
For lo! my own shall come to me.

I stay my haste, I make delays,
For what avails this eager pace?
I stand amid the eternal ways,
And what is mine shall know my face.

Asleep, awake, by night or day,
The friends I seek are seeking me;
No wind can drive my bark astray,
Nor change the tide of destiny.

What matter if I stand alone?
I wait with joy the coming years;
My heart shall reap where it hath sown,
And garner up its fruit of tears.

The waters know their own and draw
The brook that springs in yonder height;
So flows the good with equal law
Unto the soul of pure delight.

The stars come nightly to the sky;
The tidal wave unto the sea;
Nor time, nor space, nor deep, nor high,
Can keep my own away from me.

—John Burroughs